MODERN BRITISH
ARMOU
FIGH
VEHI
TERRY GA

A survey of all types currently
in service, from Challenger to
Tracked Rapier.

MODERN BRITISH
ARMOURED
FIGHTING
VEHICLES

TERRY GANDER

Patrick Stephens, Wellingborough

First published in 1986

British Library Cataloguing in Publication Data

Gander, Terry
Modern British armoured fighting vehicles,
Military—Great
Britain
I. Title
623.74′75′0941   UG446.5

ISBN 0-85059-836-2

*Patrick Stephens Limited is part of
Thorsons Publishing Group*

Photoset in 10 on 11pt Helvetica Light
by Avocet Marketing Services, Bicester, Oxon.
Printed and bound in Great Britain on 115gsm Fineblade
Cartridge for the publishers,
Patrick Stephens Limited,
Denington Estate, Wellingborough, Northants,
NN8 2QD, England.

CONTENTS

INTRODUCTION

Nearly all the armoured vehicles described in this book are used by the armoured divisions of 1 (BR) Corps, the main combat strength of the British Army. The modern armoured division is a powerful fighting force made up of a number of brigades, usually three, and each brigade comprises three battalions or regiments — the infantry use the term battalion and the Royal Armoured Corps use the term regiment but they equate to about the same in manpower terms.

1 (BR) Corps has three armoured divisions and one infantry division. Within each armoured division there is one armoured brigade with two armoured regiments and one mechanized infantry battalion; the other two brigades each have one armoured regiment and two mechanized infantry battalions. The infantry division has three infantry brigades all formed from mechanized infantry battalions.

The armoured regiments use either Challenger or Chieftain main battle tanks (MBTs) and the mechanized infantry battalions use the FV432 armoured personnel carrier (APC) and its variants. Several infantry battalions from the United Kingdom use the wheeled Saxon APC and in time some mechanized infantry battalions will receive the Warrior APC. However, these two types of formation cannot go into battle unaided and so proceed to combat with all manner of supporting arms each with their own armoured vehicles. Some of these supporting arms are integral with the formations within the divisions but others come under the direct control of 1 (BR) Corps and are allocated to the various divisions as requested or as seen fit to suit the situation.

High on the list of these supporting arms is the artillery. Each armoured division has its own integral artillery support in the form of 155 mm M109A2s or 105 mm Abbots, both self-propelled equipments, but more support is provided by the Corps Artillery Division. This has the really heavy 8-in M110 self-propelled howitzers, the long-range 175 mm M107 self-propelled guns and the Tracked Rapiers of the Air Defence Regiments — these are all included in this volume but the Lance missiles are not as they are covered in a companion volume. The Artillery Division includes a Locating Regiment which makes much use of FV432s, often with special 'fits' to suit their specialized roles.

Also under Corps control comes the Armoured Engineer Regiment with its array of Centurion AVREs, Chieftain Bridgelayers and Combat Engineer Tractors (CETs); additionally, each armoured division has its own field engineer regiment based on the FV432 but with a whole array of specialized engineer equipment, including yet more CETs. There are also Corps signals regiments as well as the signals elements within each division, all of them using various forms of armoured vehicle such as the FV439 and converted·FV432s.

Within 1 (BR) Corps the important element of reconnaissance has recently been the subject of a shake-up to the extent that each armoured regiment and mechanized infantry battalion now has its own integral reconnaissance element in addition to the usual armoured reconnaissance regiment within each armoured division. This area is the element of the Scorpion/Scimitar series of vehicles but elements of the Scorpion range crop up all across the 1 (BR) Corps spectrum. Vehicles such as the Spartan APCs are widely used by all manner of arms from infantry to engineers and the Sultan armoured command vehicle is used by just about every formation within 1 (BR) Corps. The armoured reconnaissance regiment is also the home of the Striker anti-tank guided missile launcher while the larger FV438 is used within the guided weapon troops of each armoured regiment.

Everywhere throughout 1 (BR) Corps the Royal Mechanical and Electrical Engineers (REME) keep things moving with their array of armoured recovery and repair vehicles (ARRVs). They are all mentioned in this book and it must be remembered that without their efforts the armoured vehicles of 1 (BR) Corps would be unable to keep going for very long.

Away from 1 (BR) Corps, armoured vehicles are still used for other purposes. In Northern Ireland the venerable Pigs are still used to support the security forces and in Great Britain the wheeled Foxes are used to equip the Yeomanry, while many of the vehicles mentioned in this book are used for training or to equip reinforcement units for 1 (BR) Corps and BAOR. Mention of the Pig prompts the need to say that not all the armoured vehicles mentioned in this book are as factory-fresh as the mighty Challengers. The Centurion AVREs are now very long in the tooth while the Centurion ARVs are little younger. The nimble little Ferret scout cars soldier on for the simple fact is that there seems to be no vehicle suitable to replace them; in some eyes even the FV432s are now becoming somewhat ancient.

To offset these veterans there are some new equipments in the pipeline. The Warrior APC is on the way and one day the artillery will get MLRS. It remains to be seen if they get the 155mm SP-70 as well. Challengers still roll off the production lines and there will be new support vehicles to go with them so the Army still has plenty of new equipment to look forward to although, as the contents of this book will show, they have plenty of different types of armoured vehicle to look after already.

FV4030/4 CHALLENGER

Armament 1×120mm L11A5 gun; 1×7.62mm L8A2 machine-gun; 1×7.62mm L37A2 machine-gun; VIRSS smoke dischargers. **Crew** 4. **Weight in action** 62,000 kg. **Weight when training** 60,900 kg. **Length, gun forward** 11.56m. **Length, gun rearward** 9.80m. **Height, turret roof** 2.50m. **Height, commander's sight hood** 2.95m. **Width overall** 3.51m. **Width over tracks** 3.42m. **Track width** 0.65 m. **Ground clearance** 0.50m. **Maximum road speed** 56km/h. **Range, roads** Not released. **Vertical obstacle** 0.90m. **Maximum gradient** 58%. **Trench crossing** 2.80m. **Fording** 1.07m. **Engine** Rolls-Royce CV12 TCA 12-cylinder 26.11-litre diesel developing 1,200 bhp at 2,300 rpm. **Ammunition stowage** 120mm — 48 to 52 rounds; 7.62 mm — 4,000 rounds.

The search for a Chieftain replacement began almost as soon as the first Chieftains were entering service. The first plan was for an entirely new battle tank, known as MBT-80, to be developed jointly with West Germany but after some years the West Germans dropped out as their time scale was becoming out of phase with the British procurement schedule and for a while MBT-80 was a purely British project. It was not long before the Treasury was having qualms regarding the enormous costs involved in such a project and in the end the MBT-80 was terminated. The British Army had to contemplate an entirely new vehicle.

Fortunately, such a vehicle was at hand. As early as 1971 Iran had purchased more than 700 Chieftains and had asked for more but with some improvements incorporated. From this evolved the FV4030/2 (the Shir 1) and the FV4030/3 (the Shir 2), both of which were due to be delivered to Iran during the early 1980s. The downfall of the Shah of Iran brought an end to the project, however, leaving a production line devoid of a customer. The British Army duly stepped in to become the new customer and further development of the FV4030 series resulted in the FV4030/4, soon to be christened Challenger.

The Challenger is now in full-scale production for the British Army and already two of the five regiments destined to receive it have the Challenger in service — the 13th/18th Hussars (13/18H) receiving theirs in 1983 and the 2nd Royal Tank Regiment (2 RTR) during 1984. Challenger has made quite an impression on these two regiments for, whereas the accent for Chieftain was on firepower and protection with mobility coming a rather poor third, with the Challenger the balance is much more equal. The Challenger retains its firepower in the form of the 120mm L11 main gun (with the 120mm rifled L30 gun to replace it at some future date), and the protection is now even better as Chobham armour has been incorporated. The Challenger's mobility has been assured by the use of a Rolls-Royce CV12 TCA diesel developing 1,200

9

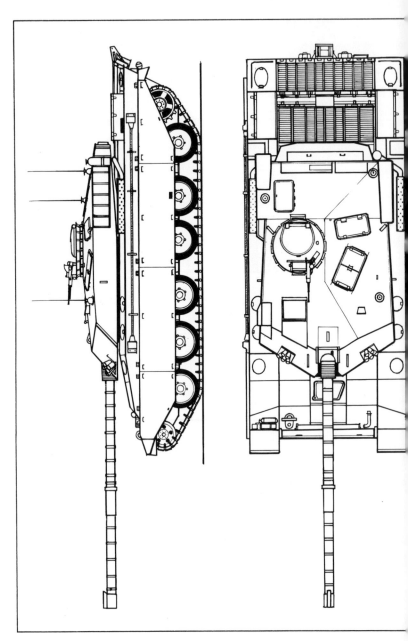

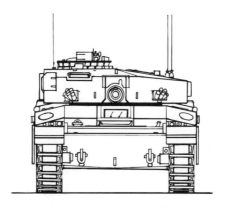

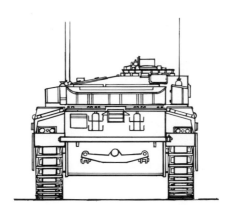

CHALLENGER MBT

1:76 scale

Two clear views showing the general layout of an early production Challenger.

bhp allied to a David Brown TN37 transmission — in time this transmission will become the TN54. The engine, transmission and cooling system are all contained in a power pack that weighs 5,488 kg and can be removed easily for repair and replacement. The power output of the engine ensures that the Challenger is much more nippy and possessed of a better all-round performance than the Chieftain which is inclined to be rather underpowered and ponderous.

Having evolved from the Chieftain, the Challenger retains some of its features. The new tank uses an IFCS fire control system very similar to that of the Chieftain but it will be allied to a new night and poor vision system known as the Thermal Observation and Gunnery System, or TOGS. Much of the Challenger's other vision and other optical devices will be familiar to Chieftain crews.

The introduction of Challenger into service has not been all plain sailing. One of its drawbacks is its combat weight, which puts it into the Class 70 load classification bracket. This means that items such as bridges, ferries and so on all have to be strengthened. The weight of the power pack is such that the REME's FV434 cannot handle it so, as an interim measure, the Chieftain ARRV has had to be introduced until the new specialist Challenger ARRV is produced. The Challenger itself is still the subject of a great deal of development work but already it is one of the most powerful fighting vehicles in the world. It is popular with its crews who rate it highly despite the fact that the Chobham armour cannot be machined to accept the various racks and stowage points that tank crews love to use to stow their personal and other gear.

Above left *Challenger showing its paces on a training ground.*
Left *A Challenger of the 14th/20th King's Own Hussars.*

FV4201 CHIEFTAIN

Data for Mark 5 — **Armament** 1×120mm L11A5 gun; 1×7.62mm L8A1 machine-gun; 1×7.62mm L37A1 machine-gun; 2×G-barrel smoke dischargers. **Crew** 4. **Weight in action** 55,000 kg. **Length, gun forward** 10.795m. **Length, gun rearward** 9.87m. **Length of hull** 7.518m. **Height, overall** 2.895m. **Width, with searchlight** 3.657m. **Width, over skirts** 3.504m. **Width, over tracks** 3.327m. **Track width** 0.61m. **Ground clearance** 0.508m. **Maximum road speed** 48 km/h. **Range, roads** 400-500 km. **Vertical obstacle** 0.914m. **Maximum gradient** 60%. **Trench crossing** 3.149m. **Fording** 1.066m. **Engine** Leyland L60 No 4 Mark 8A developing 750 bhp at 2,100 rpm. **Ammunition stowage** 120mm — 64 rounds; 7.62mm — 6,000 rounds.

Chieftain is still the most important British battle tank in numerical terrns, despite the introduction of the Challenger. It has been in service since 1967 and remains one of the most powerful battle tanks in service anywhere, thanks to a long and involved programme of in-service improvements and modifications. These changes are highlighted by a summary of the various Marks that have been produced since the first Chieftains appeared:

Mark 1   40 only, used only for training 1965/66.
Mark 2   First service model, 650 hp engine.
Mark 3   Extra equipment, various sub-marks.
Mark 4   Only two produced.
Mark 5   Uprated engine, numerous detail improvements.
Mark 6   Mark 2 with Mark 5 powerpack.
Mark 7   Mark 3 with Mark 5 powerpack.
Mark 8   Late Mark 3 with Mark 5 powerpack.
Mark 9   Mark 6 with IFCS.
Mark 10   Mark 7 with IFCS.
Mark 11   Mark 8 with IFCS.
Mark 12   Mark 5 with IFCS.

A study of the above list, which is over-simplified mainly because a complete listing of all the detailed changes would more than fill this book, will reveal two main items, the introduction of an uprated engine and the introduction of something called IFCS. To deal with the engine first, it must be mentioned that, ever since it was introduced, the engine has been the Chieftain's main trouble spot. When the Chieftain was still in the early development stage it was decided to use the Leyland L60 multi-fuel engine in a removeable engine pack but, for various reasons, not the least of which was the selection of the multi-fuel concept technical blind

Above *A line of Chieftains on the Lulworth ranges.*

Below *Somewhere under the concealing foliage is a Chieftain.*

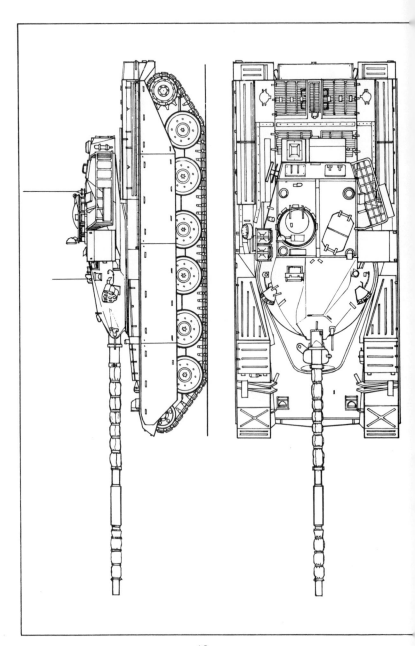

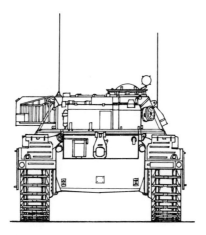

CHIEFTAIN MBT

1:76 scale

alley, the L60 was unable to produce its planned power output. The first models produced only 650 hp instead of the planned 700 hp and by the time the output was increased to the proper figure other technical shortcomings had led to the Chieftain being overweight. The result was that for many years Chieftains were prone to a seemingly never-ending series of engine problems and unreliability, but by the late 1970s a variety of improvements had done away with the worst of them although the output has remained at 750 hp and the Chieftain is still a rather ponderous vehicle in the field.

However, the Chieftain more than makes up for this lack of mobility by having considerable protection for the crew (up till the introduction of Challenger the interior of a Chieftain was considered one of the safest places to be on a battlefield) and a very powerful 120mm main armament. This gun can knock out other battle tanks at considerable ranges but it is no good without a good fire control system and this is where IFCS comes in. For many years the main gun was 'ranged' by

Right *Inside the turret, the commander of a Chieftain.*
Below *Chieftains at the Suffield training area in Canada.*

using a machine-gun over the barrel that fired special tracer rounds with a similar ballistic trajectory to the 120mm main gun. This system was not particularly accurate so in the age of the computer the Improved Fire Control System (IFCS) was introduced. IFCS is based around a central GEC-Marconi 12-12P computer which handles all the variables likely to affect gun performance using items such as wind sensors scattered around the hull and turret —even factors such as gun trunnion angle and external temperature are taken into account. By laying the gun sight graticule on a target the IFCS can range accurately, allow for the movement of the target by taking turret traverse rates into account, off-set for a number of other variables, and deliver the first round on or very near the target. Variables are kept to an absolute minimum and even the main 120mm gun barrel is lagged to prevent the wind from cooling one side of the barrel more than the other and thus producing slight warping.

There is a machine-gun co-axial with the main gun and the commander has another on his cupola which can be elevated to provide some small degree of anti-aircraft protection. Turret-located smoke dischargers provide concealment when necessary and the all-important vision devices are kept free from dust by the side skirts, which also act as defensive stand-off plates against hollow charge projectiles.

The turret contains the loader to the left of the large gun breech (looking forwards) while to the right are the gun layer with the commander seated behind and above him. The driver is positioned centrally at the front of the hull on a special seat that allows him to recline when closed down — he then uses special periscopes to see ahead. The interior of the turret is rather cramped and full of radios and other gear (there are two Clansman VRC 353 sets) including such items as a NBC pack and a water boiler for the tea.

An extra 'bolt-on' piece of equipment is a dozer blade to dig tank slots and other earthworks. At least one tank in every troop is fitted with this.

Chieftain variants include the FV4205 Bridgelayer and the FV4204 Armoured Recovery Vehicle (ARV) — one derivative of the latter is the Armoured Repair and Recovery Vehicle used with the Challenger regiments.

FV4204 ARMOURED RECOVERY VEHICLE

Data for ARRV — **Armament** 1×7.62mm L37A1 machine-gun; 2×6-barrel smoke dischargers; 2×4-barrel smoke dischargers. **Crew** 4. **Weight** 55,640 kg. **Length** 8.57m. **Height** 3.43m. **Width, over blade** 3.53m. **Width, over tracks** 3.33m. **Track width** 0.61m. **Ground clearance** Approx 500mm. **Maximum road speed** 42.4 km/h. **Range, roads** 400-500 km. **Vertical obstacle** 0.902m.**Maximum gradient** 70%. **Trench crossing** 3.15m. **Fording** 1.066m. **Engine** Leyland L60 No 4 Mark 8A developing 750 bhp at 2,250 rpm. **Ammunition stowage** 7.62mm — 1,600 rounds; Smoke grenades — 20.

The FV4204 ARV is based on the hull and suspension of the Chieftain Mark 5 but many changes have been made to convert the tank to the ARV role. For a start there is no turret and the driver's position has been switched to the left to make more room for the main winch. At the front of the hull is a dozer blade, not for earth shifting (although it can be used for this purpose) but for providing an earth anchor when the main winch is in use. This winch has a normal pulling capacity of 30,000 kg but with the dozer blade dug in this can be increased to as much as 90,000 kg. There is also a 3,000 kg secondary winch. Both winches are driven via a power take-off from the main engine.

The only armament carried is a single machine-gun on the commander's cupola although there are smoke dischargers front and rear. The top of the vehicle is liberally covered with all manner of recovery gear and special tools.

FV4204 Chieftain armoured recovery vehicle (ARV).

With the introduction into service of the Challenger MBT the Chieftain ARV has been joined by the Chieftain ARRV (Armoured Repair and Recovery Vehicle). This retains all the recovery abilities of the ARV but it also has a repair function as it has a side-mounted hydraulic crane to make engine pack changes on the Challenger MBT. This variant was originally produced for Iran but with the loss of that contract it has been switched to the British Army until the Challenger ARRV enters production some time during 1988. Like the Chieftain ARV and ARRV before it, the Challenger ARRV will be built by Vickers Defence Systems at Newcastle upon Tyne. The Challenger ARRV will be based on the chassis and engine pack on the Challenger MBT and, like the Chieftain ARRV, will not only have a side-mounted crane but a rack for a spare engine pack over the rear hull.

Right *Spare engine rack on a Chieftain ARRV Mark 2.*

Below *Chieftain armoured recovery and repair vehicle (ARRV).*

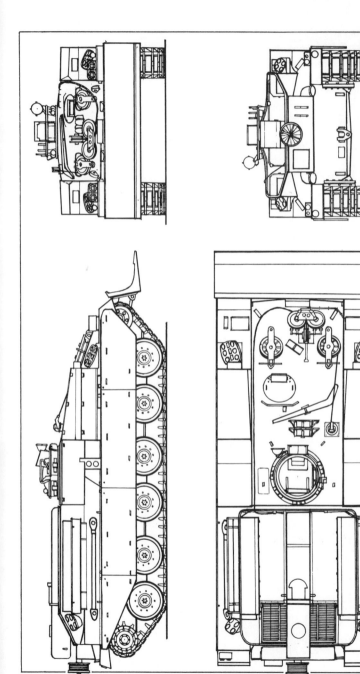

CHIEFTAIN ARV 1:76 scale

FV4205 BRIDGELAYER

Data for FV4204 with No 8 Bridge — **Armament** 2×7.62mm L7A2 machine-guns; 2×6-barrel smoke dischargers. **Crew** 3. **Weight in action** 53,300 kg. **Length, with bridge** 13.741m. **Length of hull** 7.52m. **Height with bridge** 3.923m. **Width with bridge** 4.165m. **Width over skirts** 3.504m. **Width over tracks** 3.33m. **Track width** 0.61m. **Ground clearance** Approx 500mm. **Maximum road speed** 48 km/h. **Range, roads** 400 km. **Vertical obstacle** 0.90m. **Maximum gradient** 60%. **Trench crossing** 3.00m. **Fording** 1.066m. **Engine** Leyland L60 No 4 Mark 7A developing 730 bhp at 2,100 rpm. **Ammunition stowage** 7.62mm — 3,200 rounds.

No 8 Tank Bridge — **Weight** 12,200kg **Length** 24.384m. **Max span, firm banks** 22.86m. **Width overall** 4.012m.

No 9 Tank Bridge — **Weight** 9144 kg. **Length** 13.411m **Max span, firm banks** 12.192m **Width overall** 4.156m.

The first Chieftain Bridgelayers were issued to the Army in 1974 following a rather protracted development period lasting over a decade. They are used by only one regiment, 32 Armoured Engineer Regiment, Royal Engineers, who are based in BAOR under 1 (BR) Corps control.

A complete Chieftain Bridgelayer has four components: the bridgelayer itself, the two bridges — one a No 8 and the other the shorter No 9 — and finally the Crusader tractor and semi-trailer used to carry the spare bridge. The larger of the two bridges is the No 8 Tank Bridge which is of the scissors type. When travelling it is carried on a rack over the

Chieftain bridgelayer carrying a No 9 bridge.

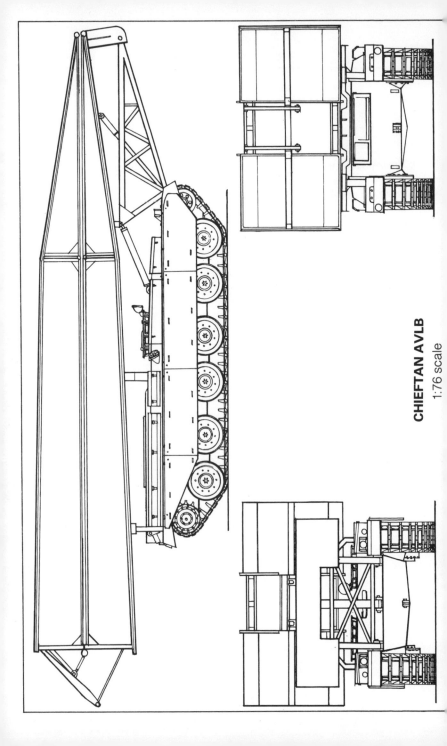

CHIEFTAN AVLB

1:76 scale

Above *FV4205 with No 8 bridge.*   **Below** *Laying a No 8 bridge.*

turretless hull. On arrival at a bridging site, which has usually been the subject of a careful reconnaissance, the bridge is laid in three stages using a hydraulic system under the control of the driver. If the gap to be crossed is too wide for one bridge, another may have to be laid on to the end of the first. The entire process for a single-span bridge takes from three to five minutes with the recovery phase, from either end, taking about ten minutes. The No 9 Tank Bridge is a single-span bridge laid in about the same time as the No 8.

Chieftain Bridgelayers may now be seen fitted with mine ploughs to increase their utility and tactical flexibility when not in use for the bridgelaying role. A new type of Chieftain Bridgelayer known as the Mark 6 will soon be entering service to supplement the numbers already in use. The No 6 is a factory conversion of early Marks of Chieftain MBT to the bridging role and they will have more powerful hydraulic systems and other changes. They will be about 3,000 kg heavier than the existing Chieftain Bridgelayers.

FV101 SCORPION

Armament 1×76mm L23A1 gun; 1×7.62mm L43A1 machine-gun; 2×4-barrel smoke dischargers. **Crew** 3. **Weight in action** 8,073 kg. **Length overall** 4.794m. **Height** 2.102m. **Width overall** 2.235m. **Width over tracks** 2.134m. **Track width** 0.432m. **Ground clearance** Approx 356mm. **Maximum road Speed** 80.5 km/h. **Range, roads** 644 km. **Vertical obstacle** 0.50m. **Maximum gradient** 60%. **Trench crossing** 2.057m. **Fording** 1.067m. **Engine** Jaguar J60 No 1 Mark 100B 4.2-litre 6-cylinder petrol developing 190 hp at 4,750 rpm. **Ammunition stowage** 76mm — 40 rounds; 7.62mm — 3,000 rounds.

When the development programme that led to the FV101 Scorpion series began in the early 1960s it was decided that the resultant vehicle would be lighter, faster and better-armed than the vehicles then in

Below and overleaf *FV101 Scorpion travelling flat out forwards...and backwards!*

service — the Ferrets, the FV601 Saladin and the FV603 Saracen. The need for air transportation imposed a weight limit of 8,200 kg and the new vehicle was supposed to carry out a whole range of roles, mainly reconnaissance, fire support and anti-tank fire. The weight limitation meant that no one vehicle could accomplish all these design requirements so a range of vehicles was produced of which the FV101 Scorpion is the 'base'.

By 1967 the project was at the prototype stage and by 1972 the first full production model was ready. The main British production run was over 2,000 vehicles — more went to the Belgian Army and the Scorpion series has turned out to be one of the British defence industry's major export successes. The main production contract went to Alvis Limited of Coventry, now part of the United Scientific Group.

The FV101 Scorpion is a very compact vehicle which makes use of aluminium armour to keep weight down. Early production models used swimming screens that could be raised to allow the vehicle to become fully amphibious but these have now been removed from most British Army examples. The turret has the commander to the left and the gunner to the right. Originally the co-axial machine-gun was used for ranging the

An early production Challenger still fitted with conventional smoke dischargers.

Above left *Challenger MBT fitted with the new Visual and Infra-Red Screening System (VIRSS) on the front of the turret, which conceals the precise location of the vehicle from both optical and infra-red detection.*

Left *An Army Gazelle helicopter with a Chieftain of the Royal Armoured Corps.*

Above *A Scorpion demonstrates its cross-country agility.*

Above *A Fox armoured car on patrol in Germany.*

Below *A FV432 ambulance of the Irish Guards during an exercise.*

main 76mm gun but a programme to install laser-based rangefinding equipment is now under way and a thermal imaging system is also being installed — the L43A1 machine-gun being retained as a turret co-axial weapon. Apart from these changes the FV101 Scorpion (and the rest of the Scorpion series) is still subject to a great deal of modification as part of a mid-service life programme. Some changes apparently involve the engine which is based on the well-known Jaguar 4.2-litre but de-rated. The turret houses a NBC system.

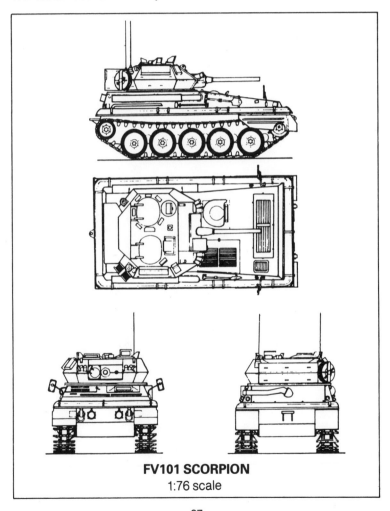

FV101 SCORPION
1:76 scale

It should be stressed that the Scorpion is not a light tank but a reconnaissance vehicle. Its 76mm main gun has only a limited performance against MBTs but is quite effective against lighter armoured targets such as other reconnaissance vehicles. The L23A1 can fire HESH, HE, smoke and a canister round for use against infantry in the open at close ranges.

It is known that the Army is looking at ways in which the combat efficiency of the FV101 Scorpion can be improved and still more equipment and/or modifications may be introduced. In the meantime the Scorpion has been used in action during the 1982 Falkland Islands campaign where its ability to operate under the local boggy conditions and good general all-round performance has led to the vehicle being considered for use by 5 Airborne Brigade.

FV102 STRIKER

Armament 10×Swingfire missiles; 1×7.62mm L37A1 machine-gun; 2×4-barrel smoke dischargers. **Crew** 3.**Weight in action** 8,346 kg. **Length overall** 4.826m. **Height** 2.28m. **Width overall** 2.28m. **Width over tracks** 2.134m. **Track width** 0.432m. **Ground clearance** Approx 356mm. **Maximum road speed** 80.5 km/h. **Range, roads** 483 km. **Vertical obstacle** 0.50m. **Maximum gradient** 60%. **Trench crossing** 2.057m. **Fording** 1.067m. **Engine** Jaguar J60 No 1 Mark 100B 4.2-litre 6-cylinder petrol developing 190 hp at 4,750 rpm. **Ammunition stowage** Swingfire missiles — 10 rounds; 7.62mm — 3,000 rounds.

The FV102 Striker entered service in 1978 and is now employed by the reconnaissance regiments allotted to 1 (BR) Corps. It uses the same suspension and automotive components as fitted to the FV101 Scorpion but the hull is more similar in shape and outline to that of the FV103 Spartan (see next entry). However, at the hull top rear are five racks for launching Swingfire anti-tank missiles 'with space inside the hull for a

FV102 Striker with missile bins lowered.

further five. The resemblance to Spartan is no coincidence for on a battlefield the Striker would so resemble the Spartan as to conceal its anti-tank role — most similar anti-tank missile carriers have their hulls and turrets strewn with missiles that can be seen readily by an enemy and accordingly be marked down for elimination. With Striker, an enemy

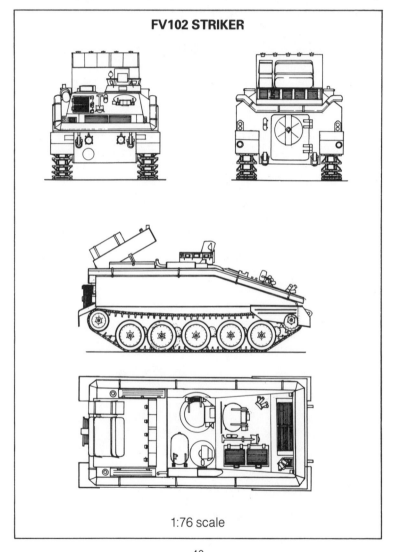

FV102 STRIKER

1:76 scale

Above *Striker with Swingfire missiles ready to fire.*

Overleaf *Clear shot of a Striker with its missile bins raised.*

would be hard put to recognize it for what it was until the bins on the roof were raised for launching.

The Swingfire missiles used with Striker have a range potential of 4,000 m but are usually launched at ranges lower than that. Each missile weighs 28 kg and has a HEAT warhead —guidance is via wires that run out from the tail of each missile. The missiles can be fired and guided either from within the vehicle (using the cupola as the guidance point) or from a remote control unit up to 100 m away from the vehicle. Once all five missiles have been fired they have to be reloaded from outside the vehicle. A thermal imaging night sight may be used, and the sighting system incorporates a built-in simulator to keep the crew up to the somewhat tricky task of guiding the missile on to a target.

FV103 SPARTAN

Armament 1×7.62mm L37A1 machine-gun; 2×4-barrel smoke dischargers **Crew** 3+4. **Weight in action** 8,172 kg. **Length** 4.93m. **Height** 2.26m. **Width overall** 2.257m. **Width over tracks** 2.134m. **Track width** 0.432m. **Ground clearance** Approx 356 mm. **Maximum road speed** 80.5 km/h. **Range, roads** 483 km. **Vertical obstacle** 0.50m. **Maximum gradient** 60%. **Trench crossing** 2.057m. **Fording** 1.067m. **Engine** Jaguar J60 No 1 Mark 100B 4.2-litre 6-cylinder petrol developing 190 bhp at 4,750 rpm. **Ammunition stowage** 7.62mm — 3,000 rounds.

The FV103 Spartan may be regarded as the armoured personnel carrier component of the Scorpion range but the British Army does not use it in that capacity. Instead it employs the Spartan as a carrier for taking specialist personnel around the battlefield. These specialists are many and varied and may include Blowpipe/Javelin missile teams, Royal

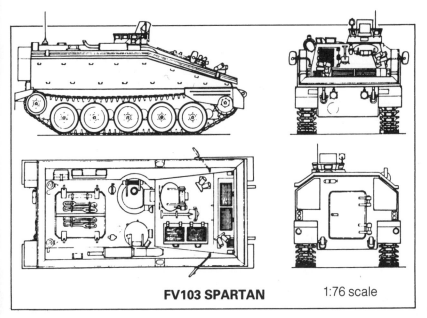

FV103 SPARTAN 1:76 scale

Left *FV103 Spartan armoured personnel carrier (APC).*

Below *FV103 with Milan Compact Turret (MCT).*

Engineer combat engineer troop commanders, Striker missile re-supply teams and other´such technicians.

Spartan can carry up to four men in the hull rear and the vehicle crew may be three men, although some applications require only two. The cupola is fitted with a machine-gun as the vehicle's only armament apart from the crew's personal weapons, but a special version fitted with a Milan turret known as the Milan Compact Turret (MCT) will be issued in the near future. Milan teams are already carried by Spartans in mechanized infantry battalions but the teams have to dismount for firing. With the MCT the missiles are fired from a twin-Milan launcher on the roof, and up to eight more missiles can be carried inside the vehicle.

FV104 SAMARITAN

Armament 2×4-barrel smoke dischargers. **Crew** 2 or 3. **Weight** 8,664 kg. **Length** 5.067m. **Height** 2.416 m. **Width overall** 2.242 m. **Width over tracks** 2.134 m. **Track width** 0.432 m. **Ground clearance** Approx 356 mm. **Maximum road speed** 72.5 km/h. **Range, roads** 483 km. **Vertical obstacle** 0.50 m. **Maximum gradient** 60%. **Trench crossing** 2.057 m. **Fording** 1.067 m. **Engine** Jaguar J60 No 1 Mark 100B 4.2-litre 6-cylinder diesel developing 190 bhp at 4,750 rpm. **Ammunition stowage** Nil.

The FV104 Samaritan is the armoured ambulance component of the Scorpion range of vehicles and uses the same box hull as the FV105 Sultan (see next entry). The first Samaritan entered service in 1978 and being an ambulance it carries no armament other than two smoke dischargers for self protection. The crew may be only two with the commander acting as a medical attendant but under combat conditions it is expected that a third crew member will act as the medical attendant leaving the commander to look after the vehicle. Under these conditions up to four stretcher cases can be carried, or five seated cases, or two stretcher and three seated cases. The hull interior is entered via a large door at the rear and there is room for the stowage of medical supplies on the roof or in racks at the rear. There is also some provision for limiting internal noise and there are location points for first aid equipment on the ceiling and walls.

Unloading a simulated casualty from a FV104 Samaritan.

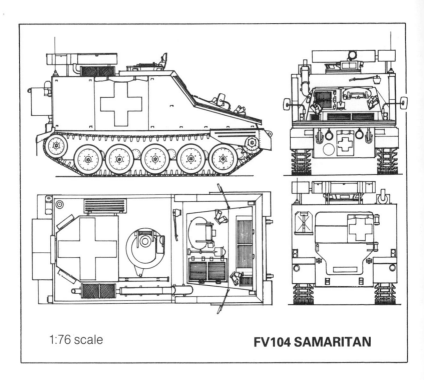

1:76 scale

FV104 SAMARITAN

Below *A Samaritan armoured ambulance on the move.*

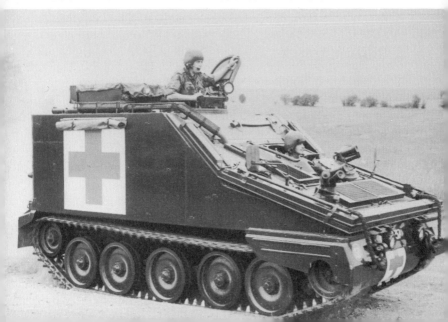

FV105 SULTAN

Armament 1×7.62mm L7A2 machine-gun; 2×4-barrel smoke dischargers. **Crew** 5 or 6. **Weight in action** 8,664 kg. **Length** 4.8m. **Height** 2.559m. **Width overall** 2.254 m. **Width over tracks** 2.134m. **Track width** 0.432m. **Ground clearance** Approx 356mm. **Maximum road speed** 72.5 km/h. **Range, roads** 483 km. **Vertical obstacle** 0.50m. **Maximum gradient** 60%. **Trench crossing** 2.057m. **Fording** 1.067m. **Engine** Jaguar J60 No 1 Mark 100B 4.2-litre 6-cylinder petrol developing 190 bhp at 4,750 rpm. **Ammunition stowage** 7.62mm — 2,000 rounds. **Penthouse length** 2.591m. **Penthouse height** 2.235m. **Penthouse width** 2.134m.

The FV105 Sultan shares the same hull shape as the FV104 Samaritan in that it has a raised roof to accommodate the occupants who have to work in the interior. The FV105 Sultan is the command and control component of the Scorpion range of vehicles and can accommodate up to six personnel in its interior. Much of the interior space is taken up with such command paraphernalia as extra radios, map tables, wall charts, additional lighting and so forth. There is usually one swivelling chair for the use of the commanding officer himself. The CO is not usually the vehicle commander, who is housed under his usual roof cupola, the rest of the vehicle crew being a radio operator and driver — the commander may well operate a second radio. These command vehicles are subject to a great deal of coming and going by people who either require orders

FV105 Sultan with its penthouse stowed on the front.

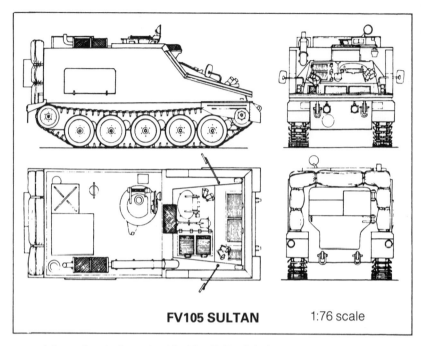

FV105 SULTAN   1:76 scale

or information, to the extent that the Sultan interior cannot accommodate them all. As a result a collapsible 'penthouse' tent is usually mounted over the rear doors when the vehicle is in use as a command post. When on the move this penthouse is either stowed over the front hull or on the roof. Also stowed on the front hull is a collapsible radio aerial. The roof is additionally used to carry racks for the crew's personal gear and other items.

The only armament carried under normal circumstances is a L7A2 machine-gun for local defence, but the crew's personal weapons may also be used. The machine-gun may be mounted on a roof pintle.

The FV105 is being considered as a carrier for various forms of electronic warfare (EW) systems. It should also be noted that in some units FV103 Spartans are used for the command role but usually only at low command levels.

FV106 SAMSON

Armament 1×7.62mm L7A2 machine-gun; 2×4-barrel smoke dischargers.
Crew 3. **Weight in action** 8,738 kg. **Length** 5.004m. **Height** 2.254m. **Width overall** 2.43m. **Width over tracks** 2.134m. **Track width** 0.432m. **Ground clearance** Approx 356mm. **Maximum road speed** 72.5 km/h. **Range, roads** 483 km. **Vertical obstacle** 0.50m. **Maximum gradient** 60%. **Trench crossing** 2.057m. **Fording** 1.067m. **Engine** Jaguar J60 No 1 Mark 100B 4.2-litre 6-cylinder petrol developing 190 bhp at 4,750 rpm. **Ammunition stowage** 7.62mm — 2,000 rounds.

The FV106 Samson armoured recovery vehicle was actually the last of the Scorpion range of vehicles to go into production (during 1978-79) and in monetary terms it is probably also the most expensive. In basic terms it is a FV103 Spartan re-arranged for the recovery role. The main change is to the rear hull interior which houses a winch powered from the main engine. This winch has 229m of wire rope and can be driven at

Below and overleaf *Two views of a F106 Samson dug in to use its winch.*

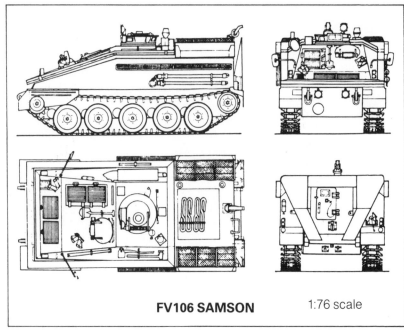

FV106 SAMSON

1:76 scale

a variable rate of up to 122m a minute. The maximum pull, with a 4:1 snatch block, is 12,000 kg enabling the FV106 Samson to recover vehicles up to the size of the FV432. For this the Samson has to lower and dig in its large rear-mounted earth spade — in practice the spade is lowered and the vehicle is then driven back on to it to dig it into the ground to provide a firm working anchor. Other equipment carried includes a small jib crane, also driven from the main engine, various tow bars, tow cables, joists and all the other bits and pieces used in the recovery role. An A-frame can be erected on the front hull to allow light vehicle components to be changed in the field.

The interior of the Samson is rather cramped as the main winch takes up much of the available space. Access to the rear is not easy as the hatch is rather small. To one side of the hatch a bench vice is mounted on a bracket, and other tools are carried.

FV107 SCIMITAR

Armament 1×30mm L21 Rarden gun; 1×7.62mm L37A1 machine-gun; 2×4-barrel smoke dischargers. **Crew** 3. **Weight in action** 7,750 kg. **Length, gun forward** 4.985m. **Length of hull** 4.794m. **Height** 2.102m. **Width overall** 2.235m. **Width over tracks** 2.134m. **Track width** 0.432m. **Ground clearance** Approx 356mm. **Maximum road speed** 80.5 km/h. **Range, roads** 644 km. **Vertical obstacle** 0.50m **Maximum gradient** 60%. **Trench crossing** 2.057m. **Fording** 1.067m. **Engine** Jaguar J60 No 1 Mark 100B 4.2-litre 6-cylinder petrol developing 190 bhp at 4,750 rpm. **Ammunition stowage** 30mm — 165 rounds; 7.62mm — 3,000 rounds.

Despite having the highest FV number in the Scorpion series, the FV107 Scimitar was the second variant to go into production, entering service during 1971. In simple terms the Scimitar is a close relative of the FV101 Scorpion and uses a generally similar turret, the main difference being that it mounts a 30mm Rarden gun in place of the 76mm L23 gun of the

FV107 Scimitar — the author is driving!

54

FV107 SCIMITAR

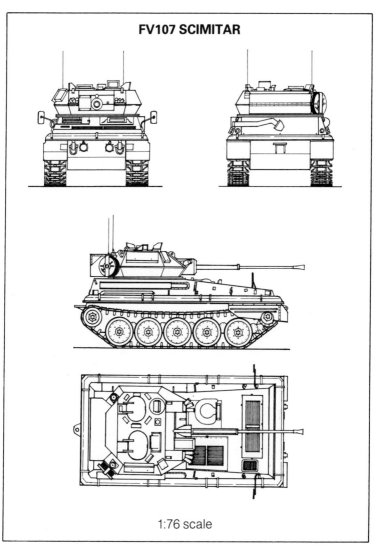

1:76 scale

Scorpion. The 30mm L21 Rarden gun is a very accurate weapon that falls into a category known as cannon. It fires at a cylic rate of eighty to ninety rounds a minute using ammunition based on designs. A recent addition to this range of ammunition has been a APDS-T round, to be added to the existing range of HEI, HE, AP and APSE.

Background photograph *Scimitars on exercises in Norway.*

Inset *A very clean Scimitar showing its 30 mm Rarden cannon to advantage.*

The Rarden-armed Scimitar is used as the main reconnaissance vehicle of the armoured reconnaissance regiments in BAOR. The equivalent regiments based in the United Kingdom use a mix of Scimitars and Scorpions. At the lowest level, both types of regiment use their reconnaissance vehicles in four-vehicle troops that are usually organized as two or three to a squadron.

Apart from the reconnaissance role the Scimitar has many other uses. It is deployed in all manner of ways ranging from general patrols of rear areas to providing fire cover for battlefield obstacles such as minefields. On the battlefield the accurate 30mm Rarden gun means that the Scimitar can deal with light armoured targets such as enemy armoured personnel carriers but it has only a limited performance against heavier tank armour.

FV721 FOX

Armament 1×30mm L21 Rarden gun; 1×7.62mm L8A1 machine-gun; 2×4-barrel smoke dischargers. **Crew** 3. **Weight in action** 6,368 kg. **Length, gun forward** 5.08m. **Length of hull** 4.166m. **Height overall** 2.20m. **Height to top of turret** 1.981m. **Width** 2.134m. **Wheel track** 1.753m. **Ground clearance** 0.30m. **Wheelbase** 2.464m. **Maximum road speed** 104 km/h. **Range, roads** 430 km. **Vertical obstacle** 0.50m. **Maximum gradient** 58%. **Trench crossing** 1.22m with channels. **Fording** 1.00m. **Engine** Jaguar J60 No 1 Mark 100B 4.2-litre 6-cylinder petrol developing 190 bhp at 4,500 rpm. **Ammunition stowage** 30mm — 99 rounds; 7.62mm — 2,600 rounds.

The wheeled reconnaissance vehicle now known as the FV721 Fox was originally a project known as the Combat Vehicle Reconnaissance (Wheeled) or CVR(W). The project began during the early 1960s but the 'hard' development commenced during 1965 and Daimler were given a contract to build fifteen prototypes, the first of which was ready in late 1967. Production proper began in 1972, not by Daimler but by what was

A rain-washed FV721 Fox on a training area.

then the Royal Ordnance Factory at Leeds, and the Army got their first vehicles soon afterwards.

The Fox may be regarded as a wheeled Scimitar as they both use the 30mm Rarden gun mounted in similar turrets. However, the Fox is a 4×4 wheeled vehicle based on the general outline of the old Ferret scout cars, even though the final product is a much re-worked vehicle. Although at first sight the turret of the Fox appears to be the same as that of the Scorpion/Scimitar, it is actually a different shape and its internal

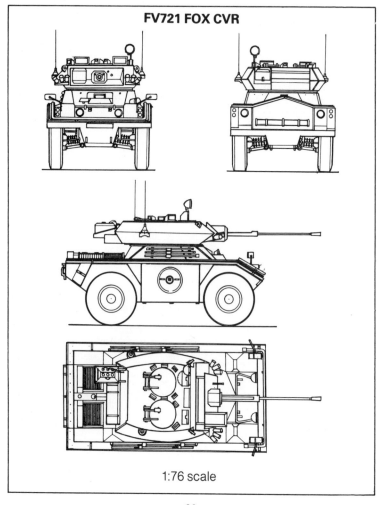

FV721 FOX CVR

1:76 scale

A Fox at speed at Bovington.

arrangements are different. The use of this turret has produced a few problems for drivers of the Fox because its relatively large weight produces a rather high centre of gravity which induces a general top-heaviness that had caused a few unfortunate accidents. Careful training is necessary to eliminate this problem.

The main users of the Fox are the TA Yeomanry regiments although some Regular reconnaissance regiments also employ them. However, the Fox still has not replaced the Ferret and is now unlikely to, for the Fox's present armed reconnaissance role is very different to the scouting role still carried out by the Ferrets in many other units.

Up to three Foxes can be carried in the cargo bay of a C-130 Hercules transport aircraft and it is possible to para-drop two on a special platform, although it is now not very likely that this facility will be much used operationally. The first production Foxes were fitted with wading screens for crossing deep water obstacles but these have subsequently been removed from most British examples.

The FV721 Fox is not used by all TA Yeomanry regiments. The Home Defence-roled Yeomanry Reconnaissance Regiments recently formed use civilian model Land Rovers only.

FV432 SERIES

Basic vehicle — **Armament** 1×7.62mm L7A2 machine-gun*; 2×3-barrel smoke dischargers. **Crew** 2+10. **Weight in action** 15,280 kg. **Length** 5.251m. **Height overall** 2.286m. **Height to top of hull** 1.879m. **Width overall** 2.80m. **Width over tracks** 2.527m. **Track width** 0.343m. **Ground clearance** 0.406m. **Maximum road speed** 52 km/h. **Range, roads** 480 km. **Vertical obstacle** 0.61m. **Maximum gradient** 60%. **Trench crossing** 2.05m. **Fording** 1.066m. **Engine** Rolls-Royce K60 No 4 Mark 4F 6.57-litre 6-cylinder multi-fuel developing 240 bhp at 3,750 rpm. **Ammunition stowage** 1,600 rounds plus.

This entry deals only with the basic FV432 and its variants. Versions with their own FV numbers (FV433 Abbot, FV434, FV438 and FV439) are covered separately.

The FV432 armoured personnel carrier can trace its origins back to the Universal and Bren Gun Carriers of the pre-war era, but in more modern terms it can be traced back to the FV420 series from which evolved the FV430 series. The FV431 would have been an armoured

*FV432s other than infantry versions often mount the 7.62 mm L4A4 (Bren) machine-gun.

A very typical FV432 ploughing through the mud on Salisbury Plain.

FV432

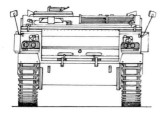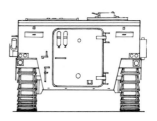

1:76 scale

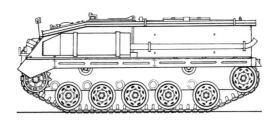

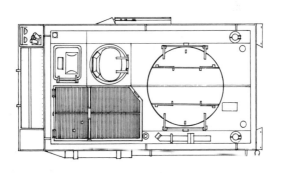

FV432 in ambulance form.

load carrier but it was not produced. The FV432 was designed to be an armoured personnel carrier and this was placed in production by GKN Sankey during 1962. By the time production ended in 1971 about 3,000 FV432s had been completed. The first production versions were the Mark 1 and Mark 1/1 which were powered by a petrol engine. On the Mark 2 this was replaced by the current multi-fuel engine and the last version was the Mark 2/2 with its NBC pack flush against the right-hand side of the hull.

In basic design terms the FV432 is a self-propelled armoured box carried on tracks. The engine is at the front to the left of the driver and the commander is seated behind and above him under the usual roof cupola. The rear of the hull interior has seating for up to ten fully-equipped men. Other than the large circular roof hatch over the main compartment and the rear access door, the occupants in the rear have no vision or weapon-firing ports. The only weapon that can be fired from the vehicle is the machine-gun carried on a pintle next to the commander's cupola, although it is possible to fire various weapons from the rear roof hatch. Some FV432s can be used to carry ZB298 surveillance radars on the hull roof. The armour of the FV432 is proof against most small-arms projectiles and shell splinters. When fully closed down it is also NBC-proof.

The FV432 is the main armoured personnel carrier used by the mechanized infantry battalions within BAOR but it is also employed by just about every other arm and service of the Army. It is used by the Royal Engineers to carry combat engineers, by the REME to carry field repair teams, by the Royal Signals to carry various types of radio 'fit' (not to be confused with the more specialized FV439 (qv)), and so on. In time the FV432s in some of the front-line mechanized infantry battalions will be replaced by the MCV-80 Warrior but the rest of the Army will have to go on using the FV432. The FV432 is now getting rather long in the tooth and becoming rather demanding of repairs and maintenance so it seems likely that in the future some form of up-dating or refurbishment programme will have to be introduced to keep the FV432 in service until well into the 21st century.

Listed below are some of the main variants of the basic FV432.

Command vehicle
The FV432 can be converted easily for the command role by removing the seating from the rear and replacing it with map boards, extra radios and lighting, wall charts and so on. Just about every type of unit appears to have its own preference regarding the actual nature of the 'fit' and some of these conversions include a

A Royal Artillery FV432 equipped with an internal FACE fire control computer.

'penthouse' tent that can be installed over the rear door. This penthouse measures 3.66×2.74×1.98 metres and when not in use is carried stowed on the hull sides. The usual weight of a command FV432 is about 15,500 kg and the normal crew is seven.

Ambulance

To convert the FV432 to the ambulance role all that is required is to fit racking for four stretchers, two each side. If only two stretchers are carried up to five seated casualties can be accommodated along the other side. Sliding swivel racks are used to load the stretchers into the FV432. When employed in the ambulance role, no armament other than the smoke dischargers is carried.

Cargo carrier

By removing the seats from the FV432 hull interior, or simply folding them up out of the way, up to 3,670 kg of bulk cargo such as fuel or ammunition can be carried. The FV432 is not often used in this role.

Recovery vehicle

For the recovery role a special conversion kit involving an internal winch powered by the main engine is installed in the hull rear. The winch cable is directed out to the rear through a special shortened door and an external spade is fitted to the rear to provide extra stability when recovering. The winch can move loads of up to 18,300 kg using a three-part tackle. The FV432 now appears to be rarely used in the recovery role.

Wavell and Ptarmigan

Wavell is a computer-based information system for use by high-level commanders within BAOR and Ptarmigan is a highly automated radio communication link system used bt all units within the BAOR area. They are both highly mobile systems and some of their various forms of terminals and/or switching components are now being installed in dedicated FV432s.

81mm mortar

The infantry 81mm L16A1 mortar can be carried and fired from the FV432 by mounting it on a special 360° traverse turntable for firing through the open rear roof hatch. When this is done the normal mortar baseplate and bipod are either stowed internally or carried on the hull sides. Internal racks are provided for up to 160 mortar bombs. This configuration is used by the mortar platoons of the mechanized infantry battalions. The normal crew is six and when fully loaded a mortar FV432 weighs 16,400 kg.

Above *FV432 with 7.62 mm GPMG turret.*

Below *FV432 fitted with 30 mm Rarden turret.*

Milan

The FV432 is used within BAOR to carry forward Milan anti-tank missile teams who dismount to fire their missiles. A single FV432 can carry up to four two-man teams with their Milan firing posts and up to 48 missiles.

GPMG turret

Within the mechanized infantry battalions some FV432s have been fitted with small turrets housing 7.62mm L37A1 machine-guns, a version of the L7A2 General Purpose Machine-Gun (GPMG). These turrets have a full 360° traverse and allow the barrel to be elevated to +50° to provide some measure of anti-aircraft defence. The weapon is aimed using a periscopic sight and the ammunition fired has extra tracer to allow the firer (usually the FV432 commander seated on a small seat slung under the turret) to make fire corrections more easily.

Royal Artillery versions

The Royal Artillery uses several versions of the FV432, the most easily recognized being that mounting a Cymbeline mortar detection radar on the roof. Even with the scanner folded down in the transporter position it is still very prominent.

Less easily spotted is the Field Artillery Computer Equipment (FACE) version which is a fully dedicated FV432 housing a FACE computer. This computer can provide fire orders or survey data for a battery of field artillery, and allied with the FACE is a teleprinter/typewriter.

Also used by the Royal Artillery are FV432s containing sound ranging equipment.

Royal Engineer versions

As well as using the FV432 to carry forward field engineer sections, the Royal Engineers use the vehicle to tow the Bar Minelayer which lays anti-tank Bar Mines. The mines are loaded into the layer's trough from within the cover of the FV432's hull rear.

The FV432 is also used to carry the Ranger anti-personnel mine system projector on the hull roof. These projectors are fitted with a number of magazines, each of which contains several small Ranger anti-personnel mines. These can be fired to cover a large area close to the projector. FV432s carrying the Ranger system can also tow the Bar Minelayer at the same time in order to seed an area with both anti-tank and anti-personnel mines.

Royal Engineer FV432s can also be used to tow the L3A1 Giant Viper (GV) minefield clearing system.

Royal Artillery, Royal Engineer, REME and Royal Signal FV432s usually carry the 7.62mm L4A4 (Bren) machine-gun in place of the L7A2 GPMG and its variants.

Above *A Company of the Irish Guards with their FV432s and Stalwart 6 × 6 trucks photographed from a helicopter.*

Below *A pair of Ferrets lead Chieftains of 4 RTR during an exercise in Germany.*

Above *An M109A1 in Germany prior to the introduction of the M109A2.*

Below *A Combat Engineer Tractor demonstrates its amphibious capability.*

Above *A Centurion ARV together with an FV432 (Stores) and an FV434.*

Below *Centurion AVRE 165 towing a Giant Viper mine-clearing trailer.*

Above *An Abbot 105 mm self-propelled gun.*

Below *Dramatic view of an M107 175 mm self-propelled gun.*

FV434 CARRIER, MAINTENANCE, FULL TRACKED

Armament 1×7.62mm L7A2 machine-gun or 1×7.62mm L4A4 machine-gun; 2×3-barrel smoke dischargers. **Crew** 4. **Weight in action** 17,750 kg. **Length** 5.72m. **Height overall** 2.794m. **Height to hull top** 1.891m. **Width overall** 2.844m. **Width over tracks** 2.527m. **Track width** 0.343m. **Ground clearance** Between 0.35m and 0.46m. **Maximum road speed** 47 km/h. **Range, roads** 480 km. **Vertical obstacle** 0.609m. **Maximum gradient** 60%. **Trench crossing** 2.05m. **Fording** 1.066m. **Engine** Rolls-Royce K60 No 4 Mark 4F 6-cylinder multi-fuel developing 240 bhp at 3,750 rpm. **Ammunition stowage** 7.62mm L7A2 — 1,000 rounds; 7.62 mm L4A4 — 336 rounds.

As its FV number implies, the FV434 is a member of the FV432 series of vehicles. It is a REME (Royal Mechanical and Electrical Engineers) vehicle used for repairing broken-down vehicles in the field but it has no

FV434 with working platform at rear.

FV434

1:76 scale

Above *FV434 with extra stowage boxes from a Chieftain MBT.*

Below *FV434 armoured repair vehicle towing a FV432.*

recovery capacity (other than towing) — recovery has to be carried out by other more specialized vehicles with winches.

Early FV434s were simply FV432s with a hydraulic crane on the top but development has led to the revised form the FV434 now takes. It has a partially open rear hull and the suspension has been modified for the crane role. When the lifting crane is in use the torsion bars on the front and rear axles are locked to provide extra stability. The partially open rear of the hull may be used to carry a spare power pack for vehicles up to the size of a Chieftain tank — the maximum carrying capacity is 2,703 kg. The hydraulic crane can be used to lift loads of up to 3,050 kg at a radius of 2.25 m while at a radius of 4m the maximum lift is 1,250 kg.

Some of the internal space is taken up by a workbench and tools such as a bench vice. One thing that is very noticeable on most FV434s is the extra stowage that many crews add to their vehicles. Most FV434s have all manner of extra bins and lockers festooned around them, some even having lockers added to the crane boom. An extra working platform is often fitted to the rear and many vehicles use some form of canvas cover or tilt over the rear working area to keep out the worst of the weather. The FV434 can be fitted with a wading screen but this has now been removed from most vehicles. Some FV434s also carry tow bars on their hull sides.

Ever since its introduction into service the FV434 has been able to work with and repair every armoured vehicle in Army use (apart from the larger self-propelled artillery vehicles) but the introduction of the Challenger means this will no longer be so. The main reason for this is the weight of the Challenger's power pack which is quite simply too heavy for the FV434's crane to lift. For the foreseeable future the Chieftain ARRV will therefore be deployed with the Challenger armoured regiments until the Challenger ARRV itself comes into service during the late 1980s. The FV434 will continue to be used with all other types of unit although it is foreseen that a Warrior (qv) field repair vehicle will be introduced.

FV438

Armament 14×Swingfire missiles; 1×7.62mm L7A2 machine-gun; 2×3-barrel smoke dischargers. **Crew** 3. **Weight in action** 16,200 kg. **Length** 5.105m. **Height 2.705m. Width overall** 2.972m. **Width over tracks** 2.527m. **Track width** 0.343m. **Ground clearance** 0.406 m. **Maximum road speed** 52 km/h. **Range, roads** 480 km. **Vertical obstacle** 0.609m. **Maximum gradient** 60%. **Trench crossing** 2.05m. **Fording** 1.066m. **Engine** Rolls-Royce K60 No 4 Mark 4F, 6-cylinder multi-fuel developing 240 bhp at 3,750 rpm. **Ammunition stowage** Swingfire missiles — 14; 7.62mm — 1,200 rounds.

For many years the FV438 was operated by the Royal Artillery in the long range anti-tank guided weapon (LRATGW) role but in more recent years the Royal Armoured Corps have re-assumed this role and the FV438 is now used by the Guided Weapon Troops in each of the armoured divisions.

The FV438 is a straightforward conversion of the FV432 to accommodate the Swingfire missile system. The main change is that the roof of the vehicle has been modified to take two Swingfire missile launching bins that can be raised for the actual launch. There is also a noticeable superstructure on the roof to house the missile operator who uses his periscopic sight to follow the missile towards its target, making corrections to the flight path via wires running out from the missile's tail. If the tactical situation demands it the sighting system, which now has a thermal imaging function built in, can be taken out of the FV438 and used from a remote position up to 50m from the vehicle. After firing, more missiles can be loaded into the launcher bins from within the vehicle.

FV438 Swingfire vehicle showing guidance cupola.

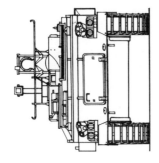
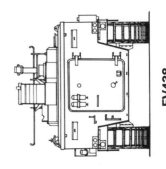

FV438

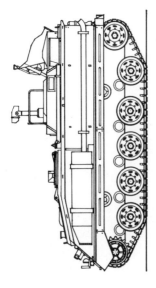
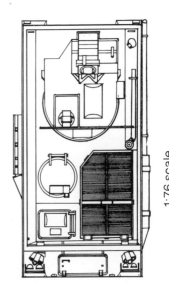

1:76 scale

FV439

It is not possible to quote any data for the FV439 Signals vehicle version of the FV432 series for there are simply too many variations among them. The usual type is a straightforward FV432 with extra gear and stowage on the roof for the hundred-and-one things the Royal Signals like to take with them into battle, and the interior is packed with communications equipment of all kinds plus a large collapsible aerial stowed on the front of the hull. A typical recent addition to this range of vehicles is the Ptarmigan switch vehicle while other '439s carry various other components of the Ptarmigan system. Some of these FV439s have more than one aerial array and some have air conditioning systems as well. Their crews vary in number but most have as their sole armament a 7.62 mm L4A4 (Bren) machine-gun that can be mounted on a pintle next to the commander's hatch.

The FV439 is a Royal Signals dedicated vehicle. Some FV432s are also used by the Royal Signals and these too are usually dedicated vehicles.

Royal Signals FV439s on railway flatcars in Germany.

FV510 WARRIOR

Data for FV510 Platoon Vehicle-Armament 1×30mm L21 Rarden gun; 1×7.62mm EX-34 Chain Gun; VIRSS smoke dischargers. **Crew** 2+8. **Weight in action** 24,000 kg. **Length** 6.34m. **Height overall** 2.735m. **Height to top of hull** 1.93m. **Width** 3.034m. **Track width** 0.46m. **Ground clearance** 0.49m. **Maximum road speed** 75 km/h. **Range, roads** 500 km. **Vertical obstacle** 0.75m. **Maximum gradient** 60%. **Trench crossing** 2.50m. **Fording** 1.30m. **Engine** Rolls-Royce CV8 TCA V-8 diesel, developing 550 hp at 2,300 rpm. **Ammunition stowage** Not released.

For many years the armoured personnel carrier now known as the Warrior was called the MCV-80 — Mechanized Combat Vehicle 80. It was first proposed during 1967 as a possible future replacement for the FV432 series and various definition studies were conducted from 1968 until 1976. Detailed design work started in 1977 but shortly after there came a period when the American M2 Bradley MICV (Mechanized Infantry Combat Vehicle) was under consideration as a less expensive alternative. However, in June 1980 it was announced that the then MCV-80 had been selected as the Army's new armoured personnel carrier which was just as well for by then three prototypes, built by GKN Sankey, were running. An initial production contract was placed with GKN Sankey during 1985.

The Warrior is to be produced in several forms. The version seen to

FV510 Warrior with 30 mm Rarden turret.

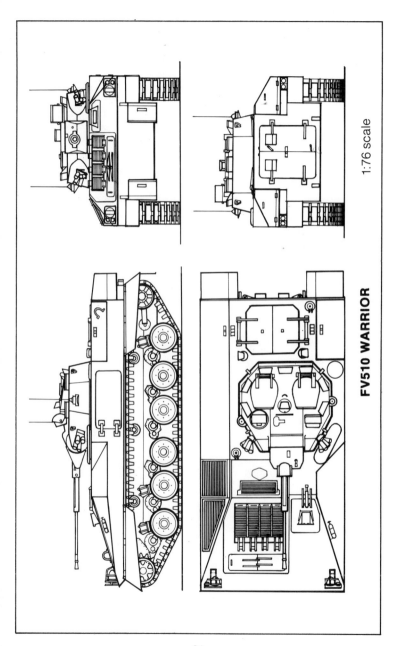

1:76 scale

FV510 WARRIOR

Reversing a Warrior.

date is the FV510 Warrior which will be produced as a Platoon Vehicle only, ie, they will only be issued one to a platoon. This version is a rather imposing looking vehicle for it has a two-man turret mounting a 30mm L21 Rarden gun with a co-axial 7.62mm Chain Gun, a machine-gun that uses an external electrical motor to power its mechanism, giving greater reliability. There is no provision for the infantry carried in the main compartment at the rear to fire their weapons from within and there are no vision ports either. There is space for eight men in the main compartment and their access to the interior is via two doors at the rear, doors that have been the subject of some criticism as on the early models they could not be opened when the vehicle was in certain positions. This door problem has now been solved by the introduction of hydraulic opening devices. The vehicle suspension is of the torsion bar type and provides the occupants with a very smooth ride over rough terrain. The comfort of the occupants has been given quite a deal of consideration for there are kit stowage points under the seats and more can be stowed in sponson-like lockers each side of the access doors. There is also a NBC kit. In short the Warrior can carry enough supplies and kit to keep its crew and the carried infantry section in action for at least 48 hours.

The FV510 Warrior's basic crew is two men, the driver and the gunner. The other occupant of the turret is the platoon commander who leaves the vehicle to go into action with his platoon leaving the gunner to provide local fire support. Incidentally, although the turret is in the middle of the vehicle it is off-set slightly to the left of the centre line.

Warrior at speed.

As has already been mentioned, the FV510 is only one version of the Warrior. The most numerous version is likely to be the ordinary section version armed only with a L7A2 GPMG in a small one-man turret. Other projected versions include a recovery vehicle with a front-mounted dozer blade, an internal winch and a GPMG turret. The GPMG turret will also be used on a version having an 81 mm mortar in the rear and firing through a roof hatch. The same turret will also appear on a combat engineer version carrying a Ranger anti-personnel mine dispenser on the roof rear. It is expected that a version that could be used either for the command or for the artillery observation role will look very much like the platoon vehicle, having a two-man turret armed with a Rarden gun. To round off this range of projected Warrior variants there will be a combat repair vehicle mounting a large hydraulic jib over the top, pivoting at the rear. This version will also use the GPMG turret. GKN Sankey are proposing other private venture versions.

It is expected that the first production Warriors will start coming off the lines during 1987 but already the Army has been using a four-vehicle section for extensive troop trials. However, there is a snag with Warrior and that is its cost. For various and depressingly familiar reasons Warrior has outrun its initial cost estimates and now the Army will not be able to obtain the numbers it initially requested. As a result Warrior will be used to equip only the front-line mechanized infantry battalions of BAOR and other units will have to go on using the FV432. It may well be that some of the proposed versions mentioned above may fall by the wayside for cost reasons and FV432s will have to remain in service for some of their roles.

SAXON

Armament 1×7.62mm L7A2 machine-gun. **Crew** 2+8 to 10. **Weight in action** 10,670 kg. **Length** 5.169m. **Width** 2.489m. **Height, commander's cupola** 2.628m. **Wheel track, front/rear** 2.08m/1.99m. **Ground clearance, axles** 0.29m. **Maximum road speed** 96 km/h. **Range, roads** 510 km. **Vertical obstacle** 0.41m. **Maximum gradient** 60%. **Fording** 1.12m. **Engine** Bedford 500 6-cylinder diesel developing 164 bhp at 2,800 rpm. **Ammunition stowage (est)** 7.62mm — 2,000 rounds.

GKN Sankey started to produce wheeled armoured personnel carriers in 1972, following their experience in building armoured bodies for the original 'Pigs' (qv). Gradual development led to the introduction of the AT105 in 1976 and from this has evolved the British Army's Saxon.

The Saxon is a rather specialized armoured personnel carrier as it is intended to act as a 'battle taxi' for infantry units based in the United Kingdom who are part of the normal 1 (BR) Corps manpower

Saxon wheeled armoured personnel carriers.

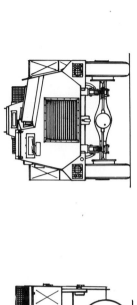

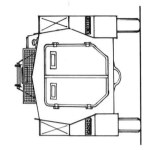

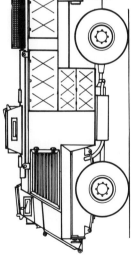

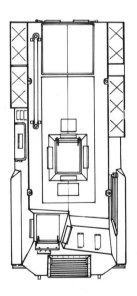

1:76 scale

SAXON APC

85

establishment. Using a wheeled carrier enables them to travel long distances with none of the disadvantages of track wear and so forth that would limit the use of tracked personnel carriers in such a 'long range' role, yet when they arrive in Germany they will still have the protection of the Saxon's armoured hull which is proof against most small-arms fire and shell splinters.

The Saxon is basically a welded steel armoured box carried on a wheeled 4×4 chassis that owes much to components taken from the Bedford MK truck series. The driver is seated well forward next to the engine while behind him is the vehicle commander. He has a roof-mounted cupola armed with a 7.62mm L7A2 machine-gun on a type of mounting known as a DISA — this can provide some form of anti-aircraft defence and may only be a temporary weapon fitting as consideration is being given to arming the Saxon with some form of 7.62mm Chain Gun mounting.

The infantry section of from eight to ten men are seated in a compartment at the rear entered through two large doors at the back — the normal capacity is eight men on long journeys. The exterior of the hull is liberally provided with stowage bins for the crew's and the occupants' gear and for some supplies for the long journey from the United Kingdom to Germany.

The Army ordered fifty Saxons in early 1983 and another 450 a year later. Early hopes that more would be ordered for the Territorial Army or other regular infantry units based in the United Kingdom appear to have come to nothing, apparently on cost grounds, so most other home-based infantry will continue to travel in trucks. The first unit to be equipped with Saxons was the 1st Battalion The King's Own Royal Border Regiment — that was in March 1984.

Apart from the personnel carrier role, some Saxons will also be used as command vehicles with a special radio and other equipment fit and there is also a special recovery version with a winch mounted on the left-hand side of the hull.

FV1611 PIG

Armament Nil — see text. **Crew** 2+6 to 8. **Weight in action** Approx 7,000 kg. **Length** 4.926m. **Height** 2.12m. **Width** 2.044m. **Wheel track** 1.713m. **Ground clearance** Not recorded. **Maximum road speed** 64 km/h. **Range, roads** 402 km. **Engine** Rolls-Royce B60 Mark 5B 4.25-litre 6-cylinder petrol developing 120 bhp at 3,750 rpm. *No other details recorded.*

The FV1611 can trace its origins back to the late 1940s when Humber produced a range of 4×4 1-ton trucks. During the early 1950s the Army found itself short of armoured personnel carriers so as a 'short term' expedient it was decided to build an armoured hull on to the truck chassis and in all about 1,700 were produced. These expedients served

A Pig on patrol in the centre of Belfast. Behind it is a Saracen — Saracens are no longer in service.

FV1611 PIG

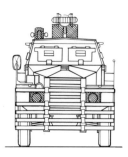 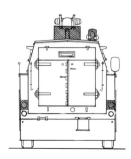

1:76 scale

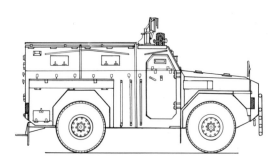

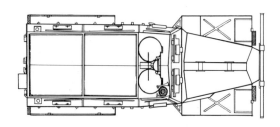

on until the late 1960s when they were withdrawn and either sold off abroad or else simply scheduled for scrap.

When the Northern Ireland security situation began to get bad the old Humber armoured personnel carriers were once more brought back into service. From storage parks all over the country the old vehicles were hurriedly culled, refurbished and sent across the Irish Sea. More were re-purchased from the sources abroad to whom they had previously been sold, and some even turned up on the Belfast quayside still in desert sand camouflage. The reason for this sudden change of course was, and still is, that the old Humbers, soon universally known as 'Pigs', were well suited to the internal security role. Being relatively small and innocuous they do not have the appearance and political drawbacks of a 'tank'. Their armoured hulls provide enough protection for the occupants and have proved to be remarkably amenable to changing operational requirements. One of the first alterations needed was more armour when local activists started using armour-piercing ammunition, so the Pigs were returned to the mainland for an up-armouring programme. This meant more weight on the chassis so suspension changes had to be made as well. Since then other modifications have been made such as fitted seats with restraining seat harnesses to protect the occupants in the case of a land mine explosion.

At one period during the early 1970s there were about 500 Pigs in use in Northern Ireland but today their numbers have been much reduced as the local situation is no longer at the level of lawlessness that once prevailed. Today Pigs are only used in regions of the Province where terrorist activity remains high, and these areas are now few. The Pigs continue to be used as personnel carriers but there are now some more specialized versions with some exotic names. Apart from the basic vehicle which is used as a carrier for personnel and explosive ordnance disposal (EOD) teams plus their equipment, there is a single-stretcher ambulance. There is also a version known as the Flying Pig which has large outwards-opening riot screens on each side. Another version that is liberally covered with wire screens for protection against RPG-7 rockets is known as the Kremlin Pig. A version with a hatch cut into the roof to allow a soldier to look out and use his rifle is known as the Holy Pig — the hatch is surrounded by perspex screens to shield against flying bricks and other missiles. Perhaps the most changed Pigs are the few that are used for patrolling along some border areas —these have machine-gun turrets taken from Shorland armoured cars set on the roof. Other more general changes include venetian blind-type steel louvres over the cab front windows to provide extra protection for the driver.

THE FERRETS

Data for Mark 1/1 — **Armament** 1×.30 L3A4 machine-gun or 1×7.62mm L4A4 machine-gun; 2×3-barrel smoke dischargers. **Crew** 2 or 3. **Weight in action** 4,210 kg. **Length** 3.835m. **Height** 1.448m. **Width** 1.905m. **Wheel track** 1.549m. **Ground clearance** 0.33m. **Maximum road speed** 93 km/h. **Range, roads** 306 km. **Vertical obstacle** 0.406m. **Maximum gradient** 46%. **Trench crossing** 1.22m with channels. **Fording** 0.914m. **Engine** Rolls-Royce B60 Mark 6A 6-cylinder petrol developing 129 bhp at 3,750 rpm. **Ammunition stowage** Up to 2,500 rounds.

The Ferret Scout Car is another of the Army's long-serving veterans for the first of them entered service back in 1952. Production did not cease until 1971 by which time 4,409 had been made, many of them for export. Several of the Ferret variants produced for the Army are no longer in use, such as the Ferret Mark 5, or FV712, which carried four Swingfire anti-tank missiles in an odd-shaped turret. The Mark 5 went out of service some years ago.

A Ferret on the Berlin border with East Germany.

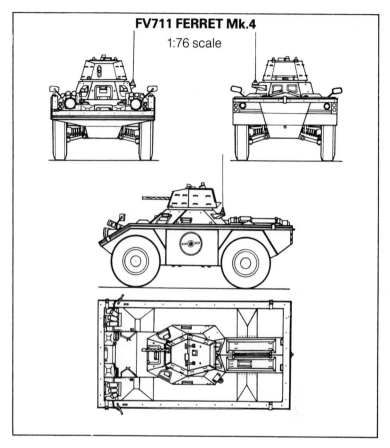

FV711 FERRET Mk.4

1:76 scale

The Ferret designations follow no logical pattern but the best way to describe them is to follow their Mark numbers. The basic model is the Mark 1/1, or FV701(J). This is an open-topped vehicle with a 4×4 drive configuration, and with armour varying from 6mm at the rear to 16mm on the superstructure and hull front and sides. The vehicle has a crew of two or three and may be armed with a 7.62mm L4A4 Bren or .30 L3A4 Browning machine-gun on a pintle — the type of machine-gun depending on the user arm. The basic layout owes much to the World War 2 Daimler Scout Car but the engine is more powerful and there are many other design changes. A canvas cover is carried to provide some protection against the elements.

The Ferret Mark 1/2 is the FV704 which is similar to the Mark 1/1 but

Above *Royal Engineers' Ferret with an extra stowage bin at the rear.*

Below *Ferret with 0.30 in Browning machine-gun in its turret.*

features a small flat-topped turret with a machine-gun mounted on an external pintle.

The next Ferret designation up the line is the Mark 2/3 (the FV701(H)), one of the most frequently encountered as it has a small turret mounting a machine-gun. It is otherwise similar to the Mark 1/1.

The Ferret Mark 3 is an updated version of the Mark 1/1 with a strengthened suspension, improved brakes and other changes to bring it up to Mark 4 standard. The Mark 4 (FV711) is a turreted Ferret, originally produced with a wading screen and extra buoyancy chambers around the hull, although the wading screens have now largely been removed.

The Ferrets still carry out their original scouting and reconnaissance roles for nearly every arm and service within the Army. Just about every branch of the Army appears to use the Ferret in some numbers and even new weapons such as the Milan anti-tank missile are carried in vehicles which form an integral part of the missile sections. The engineers and the gunners both use their Ferrets to carry out reconnaissance of working or battery sites, and the RAC use Ferrets both with their armoured regiments and armoured reconnaissance regiments. It is certainly a versatile and useful vehicle but the open-topped variants are not too popular with their crews, mainly due to their exposure to the elements. It must be stressed that the Ferrets are primarily reconnaissance vehicles and their machine-gun armament is provided purely for local protection, not for fighting other vehicles or enemy infantry. The turreted versions usually mount the .30 L3A4 Browning machine-gun, and once the Centurion AVREs are re-equipped with GPMGs, the Ferrets will be the only Army vehicles still using this particular weapon.

The Ferrets are now getting a bit long in the tooth but there is as yet no sign that their replacement is in the offing. In 1982 Alvis introduced an updated Ferret design known as the Ferret 80 but there is no sign that the Army intends to purchase this vehicle.

FV180 COMBAT ENGINEER TRACTOR

Armament 2×4-barrel smoke dischargers. **Crew** 2. **Weight in action** 17,700 kg. **Length overall** 7.30m. **Length of hull** 5.334m. **Height with anchor** 3.41m. **Height less anchor** 2.83m. **Width over bucket** 2.921m. **Width over hull** 2.87m. **Width over tracks** 2.769m. **Track width** 0.508m. **Ground clearance** 0.457m. **Maximum road speed** 56 km/h. **Maximum water speed** 2.5m/sec. **Range, roads** 320 km. **Vertical obstacle** 0.61 m. **Maximum gradient** 60%. **Trench crossing** 2.06m. **Fording** 1.83m; amphibious with preparation. **Engine** Rolls-Royce C6TFR 6-cylinder 12.17-litre diesel developing 320 bhp at 2,100 rpm. **Ammunition stowage** None.

The FV180 Combat Engineer Tractor, or CET, can trace its origins back to 1962 when a General Staff Target was issued for a vehicle that would combine the attributes of an armoured vehicle with those of an earth mover for use in forward areas. This project expanded into an international programme for a while but in the end the United Kingdom was left to go it alone and two prototypes were delivered in 1968. These were the subject of a great deal of experimentation and trials and more prototypes were delivered in late 1973 and early 1974. Production began in 1977 at the then Royal Ordnance Factory at Nottingham and first deliveries were made in May of the following year.

The CET is a unique vehicle now used by the field and other engineer regiments of the Royal Engineers. It is a very versatile vehicle that can undertake a large number of combat engineer duties from simple earthmoving and preparing tank and artillery slots to preparing the banks of water obstacles. It can also recover disabled vehicles, 'pathfind' river crossings, and so on. The CET can be used for deep wading across water obstacles but it is also amphibious with preparation and once in the water is driven by two Dowty water jets. On land the CET is normally driven with the earth-moving bucket to the rear and the crew of two sitting on the left of the hull. Both crew positions have driving controls and the CET can be driven in either direction by either crew member — both seats are reversible. The CET has a lively performance on land and in the water. To assist the vehicle when steep banks have to be climbed it carries a rocket-propelled anchor. When this is fired the CET can pull itself up using its two-speed winch (the winch has a towing capacity of up to 8,000 kg and can be used to recover stranded vehicles).

The main tool of the CET is its earth-moving bucket which has steel cutting edges and tines and a capacity of 1.91 cubic metres. Quite apart from its digging and shifting attributes the bucket can be used for a

A Combat Engineer Tractor (CET) with its digging bucket raised.

variety of other purposes. It can carry loads such as trackway and by fitting a special jib attachment to the bucket it can be used as a crane. Another attachment for the CET is a pusher bar for launching bridging equipment.

The CET's internal equipment is just as wide-ranging as its exterior features. A NBC protection pack is mounted as standard and a special cooling pack can be fitted for use in hot climates. In the British Army a Clansman 353 radio is installed. Night vision equipment can be fitted.

Production of the CET ceased in 1977 but in 1985 an order for fifty from India meant the production line could be re-started. The prospect of more vehicles for the British Army is thus very likely — one CET was lost in the Falklands campaign when it ran over a mine (with no loss to the crew) and the Royal Engineers do have a need for more.

It appears unlikely that the CET will undergo any major changes in the near future but a few slight alterations are under consideration. One is the fitting of a GPMG on a pintle near the crew hatches for at present the CET does not carry any defensive armament other than smoke dischargers, although some have been seen fitted with 7.62mm L4A4 Bren machine-guns for trials. Other possibly changes are that a dozer blade may be fitted as an optional alternative to the earth-moving bucket, while the bucket itself may be fitted with a fork lift device for lifting pallets. Routers for ripping up road surfaces are another possible option.

FV180 COMBAT ENGINEER TRACTOR
WITH LAIRD ROCKET PROPELLED ANCHOR

1:76 scale

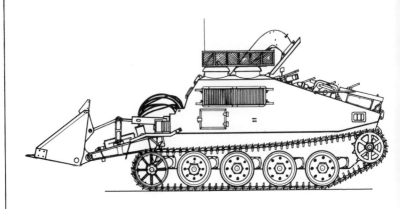

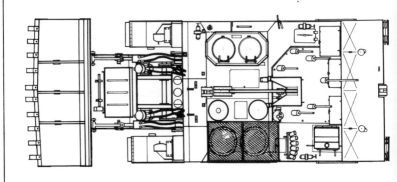

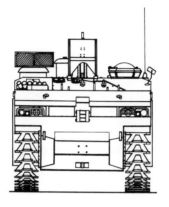

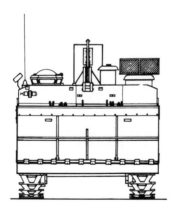

FV4003 CENTURION MARK 5 AVRE

Armament 1×165mm demolition gun or 1×105mm L7A2 gun; 2×.30 L3 machine-guns*; 2×6-barrel smoke dischargers. **Crew** 5. **Weight in action** 51,810 kg. **Length** 8.686m. **Height** 3.009m. **Width over dozer blade** 3.962m. **Width over hull** 3.39m. **Track width** 0.61m. **Ground clearance** 0.46m. **Maximum road speed** 34.6 km/h. **Range, roads** 176 km. **Vertical obstacle** 0.914m. **Maximum gradient** 60%. **Trench crossing** 3.352m. **Fording** 1.45m. **Engine** Rolls-Royce Meteor Mark IVB 12-cylinder petrol developing 650 bhp at 2,550 rpm. **Ammunition stowage** 165mm — approx 20 rounds; 105mm — not released; .30 — 3,000 rounds. **Weights and dimensions given are for AVRE 165.**

The FV4003 Centurion Mark 5 AVRE (Armoured Vehicle Royal Engineers) is another of the Army's veterans for the bulk of these vehicles were built during the early 1960s. They are used operationally by only one unit, 32 Armoured Engineer Regiment, Royal Engineers, who are based in BAOR and come under the direct command of 1 (BR) Corps.

For many years there was only one type of Centurion AVRE. This was a conversion of the Centurion Mark 5 tank to accommodate a 165mm demolition gun as the main armament and mounting a dozer blade at the front. The 165mm demolition gun fires a special HESH (High Explosive Squash Head) projectile weighing 29 kg to a maximum range of 2,400m, although its usual operational range is only half of that. This projectile is powerful enough to bring down structures such as bridges and can even be used effectively against area targets such as power stations. The dozer blade is used not only for earth-moving but is also fitted with a cradle that can carry fascines for filling-in trenches or similar obstacles, or lengths of metal trackway to form 'instant roadways' across soft terrain. These alone make the AVRE a versatile vehicle but it can also tow a special four-wheeled trailer (the FV2721) which can carry all manner of combat engineering stores. The AVRE can even be used to tow a Bar Minelayer to lay anti-tank minefields rapidly. The Centurion AVRE can also tow the Giant Viper minefield-clearing device.

The Centurion AVREs mounting the 165mm demolition gun have now been designated AVRE 165s as they have recently been joined by a version mounting a 105mm L7A2 tank gun. To differentiate these 'new' vehicles they are known as AVRE 105s. Originally they were used by the

---

* To be replaced by versions of the 7.62mm L7A2 machine-gun.

Above *Royal Engineers' Centurion AVRE 105 with mine ploughs lowered.*

Below *An AVRE 165 with mine ploughs raised in the travelling position.*

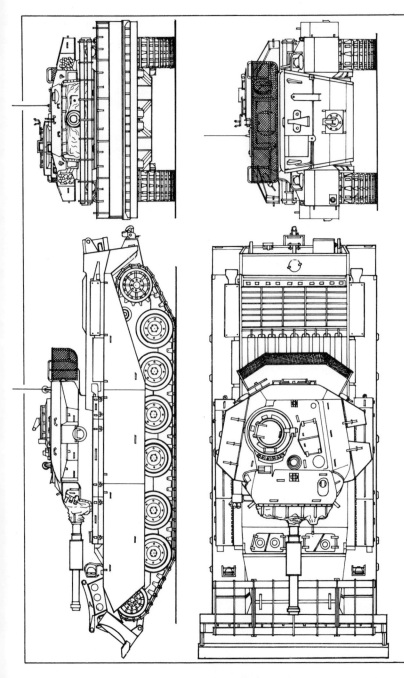

CENTURION AVRE

1:76 scale

Royal Artillery as carriers for forward observation officers but that role has now been taken over by FV432s and as the armoured engineers were expanding in numbers it was decided to convert these gun tanks for the AVRE role. The 105mm L7A2 tank guns of the AVRE 105s are used to fire HESH projectiles only — they do not fire any other type of ammunition in their AVRE role. The 105mm projectiles are not as powerful as the 165mm demolition gun projectiles but they are still effective enough for most demolition tasks. The first AVRE 105s are not fitted with dozer blades (although they can use them) but with mine ploughs. They can tow either the AVRE trailer or Giant Viper.

Operationally the Centurion AVREs are very versatile vehicles and even with the addition of the AVRE 105s it seems unlikely that there will ever be enough of them. Operating well forward with the armoured regiments, the AVREs will be used for all manner of tasks from laying assault trackway to clearing obstacles or laying minefields. The guns will be used to demolish all manner of structures and the AVREs' ability to tow supplies to the forward combat areas will no doubt be a useful asset. In any combat situation they will be among the busiest vehicles on the battlefield.

Among changes scheduled for the AVREs is a different machine-gun. At present each AVRE has a co-axial .30 L3A3 Browning machine-gun and a L3A4 mounted on a pintle next to the commander's hatch — the latter can be ground-mounted on a tripod for local defence if required. Both are due to be replaced by the appropriate forms of the 7.62mm L7A2 GPMG. Other modifications may include an update in radio fit. One change that is already underway is the replacement of the type of fascines used. Until recently the fascines were simply bundles of chesspalings or brushwood that could be produced locally —they could even be unravelled to form rough trackways across soft going. Unfortunately these fascines get very heavy when wet and they are now being replaced by bundles of plastic piping retained within strong netting. These are re-usable over and over again and when wet weigh no more than when dry.

FV4006 CENTURION ARV MARK 2

Armament 1×.30 L3A4 machine-gun; 2×5-barrel smoke dischargers. **Crew** 4. **Weight in action** 50,295 kg. **Length** 8.966m. **Height** 2.895m. **Width** 3.39m. **Track width** 0.61m. **Ground clearance** 0.45m. **Maximum road speed** 34.6 km/h. **Range, roads** 102 km. **Vertical obstacle** 0.914m. **Maximum gradient** 60%. **Trench crossing** 3.352m. **Fording** 1.45m. **Engine** Rolls-Royce Meteor Mark IVB 12-cylinder petrol developing 650 bhp at 2,550 rpm. **Ammunition stowage** .30 — 2,000 rounds.

The first Centurion ARV (Armoured Recovery Vehicle) was the Mark 1 which was little more than a tractor with a winch. It was replaced by the Mark 2 from about 1957 onwards and the Mark 2 is still in service. It is used by some armoured regiments and other units for, although it should have been replaced by the more modern Chieftain ARV, there are never enough of the latter to go round and the older Centurion ARV survives.

The Centurion ARV Mark 2 is basically a turretless version of the Centurion tank. In place of the turret is a superstructure housing a winch with a capacity of 31,000 kg — with snatch blocks this can be increased to 90,000 kg. The winch is electrically operated using power from a

Centurion ARV Mark 2 with awning over its rear area.

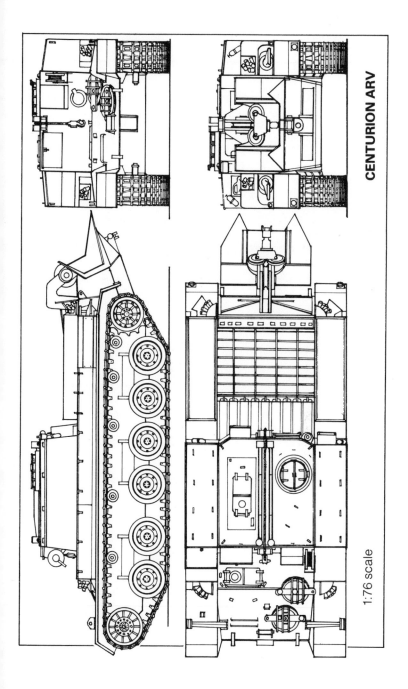

CENTURION ARV

1:76 scale

The rear spade anchor of the ARV Mark 2 can be seen here.

generator driven by a Rolls-Royce B80 petrol engine. Allied with the winch to increase the pull are large earth spades located at the rear of the vehicle. When these are lowered and dug in by reversing the vehicle, they provide a very steady anchor.

Other equipment carried on the Centurion ARV includes a 10,000 kg capacity jib crane and numerous tools and tow bars — there is even a bench vice fixed to the hull front glacis. There is no NBC system. A .30 L3A4 Browning machine-gun can be fitted on to a pintle over the commander's hatch but on some vehicles this has been replaced by a 7.62mm L4A4 Bren machine-gun.

FV433 FIELD ARTILLERY, SELF-PROPELLED, ABBOT

Armament 1×105mm L13A1 gun; 1×7.62mm L4A4 machine-gun; 2×3-barrel smoke dischargers. **Crew** 4. **Weight in action** 16,556 kg. **Length, gun forward** 5.84m. **Length of hull** 5.709m. **Height** 2.489m. **Width** 2.641m. **Track width** 0.343m. **Ground clearance** 0.406m. **Maximum road speed** 47.5 km/h. **Range, roads** 390 km. **Vertical obstacle** 0.609m. **Maximum gradient** 60%. **Trench crossing** 2.057m. **Fording** 1.219m. **Engine** Rolls-Royce K60 Mark 4G 6.57-litre 6-cylinder multi-fuel developing 240 bhp at 3,750 rpm. **Ammunition stowage** 105mm — 38 rounds (40 possible); 7.62mm — 1,200 rounds. **Maximum gun range** 17,000m. **Shell weight, HE** 16.1 kg.

The FV433 Abbot, as its designation implies, is the self-propelled artillery variant of the FV432 range. The first prototype was produced in 1961 and production proper began in 1965. Ever since then the Abbot has been the principal self-propelled weapon of the Royal Artillery field regiments in BAOR.

FV433 Abbot 105 mm self-propelled gun.

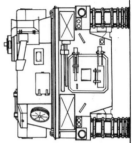
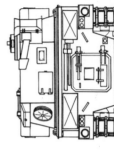

FV433 ABBOT 105mm. SP

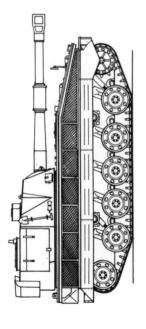
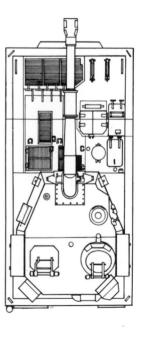

1:76 scale

The Abbot uses many components from the FV432 series but the main difference compared to the APCs is the large 360° traverse turret mounted towards the rear of the hull. This houses the three-man gun crew and the bulk of the ammunition. Although forty rounds can be accommodated, the usual load is 38, and of these six are usually HESH for the possible engagement of enemy AFVs. The gun barrel can be elevated to +70° and depressed to -5°. The ammunition is the same as that fired from the 105mm L118 Light Gun and includes HE, smoke, coloured smoke, HESH and illuminating — up to eight propelling charges can be used, depending on the range required.

The Abbot can be rendered fully amphibious through use of flotation screens which are carried folded around the top of the hull. When these are raised the vehicle can propel itself through the water by means of its tracks. Most Abbots have now had these screens removed, however, in common with other AFVs described in this book.

One variant of the Abbot developed for the Indian export market was a simplified version known as the Value Engineered Abbot. This had many of the extras such as the wading facility and NBC system required by the British Army removed . Four of these were purchased by the Army for use on the Suffield training ranges in Canada.

Analysis of recent conflicts such as those in the Middle East has indicated that the 105mm artillery calibre is now of little value against massed armoured attacks and is now regarded as obsolescent for use in any war likely to be fought in Europe. The Abbot is thus a prime candidate for replacement and when SP-70 (qv) eventually reaches service it will initially supersede the BAOR Abbots. That replacement is now long overdue, mainly as the result of the delays in the SP-70 programme. In the meantime the Abbot soldiers on and, despite its calibre drawbacks, it is still a useful and well understood weapon.

155 mm SELF-PROPELLED HOWITZER M109A2

Armament 1×155mm M185 howitzer; 1×7.62mm L4A4 machine-gun. **Crew** 6+2. **Weight in action** 24,948 kg. **Length, gun forward** 9.12m. **Length of hull** 6.19m. **Height, less machine-gun** 3.06m. **Width with fenders** 3.295m. **Width less fenders** 3.149m. **Track width** 0.381m. **Ground clearance** 0.45m. **Maximum road speed** 56.3 km/h. **Range, roads** 349 km. **Vertical obstacle** 0.53m. **Maximum gradient** 60%. **Trench crossing** 1.83m. **Fording** 1.00m. **Engine** Detroit Diesel Model 8V-71T turbocharged 8-cylinder diesel developing 405 bhp at 2,300 rpm. **Ammunition stowage** 155mm — 28 rounds; 7.62mm — 1,200 rounds. **Maximum howitzer range** 18,100m. **Shell weight, HE** 42.91 kg.

When the American 155mm M109 self-propelled howitzer first entered British Army service in 1965 it had a short 23.4-calibre

155 mm M109A2 with barrel traversed left.

barrel* known as the M126. This howitzer was used for many years until the late 1970s when a programme of re-barrelling the M109 with the longer 39-calibre M185 was started, a programme that was substantially completed by 1978. The new and longer barrel gave not only more range but a new designation for the vehicle of M109A1. This re-barrelling programme was carried out using Army facilities. During the following year, 1979, it was announced that more new 155 mm self-propelled howitzers were to be purchased direct from BMY (Bowen-McLaughlin-York) in the United States. These were to have the long barrel fitted from the word 'go' and are known as M109A2s.

The original M109 had a rather involved development history in the United States before it was purchased by the British Army, and even then it was a well-used weapon that went on to see service all over the world. In the British Army the M109A1/M109A2is used by

* The length of gun barrels is traditionally measured in calibres — ie, the number of times its length exceeds its bore. Thus a 23.4-calibre barrel of a 155mm gun is 23.4×155mm long, or 3.627m.

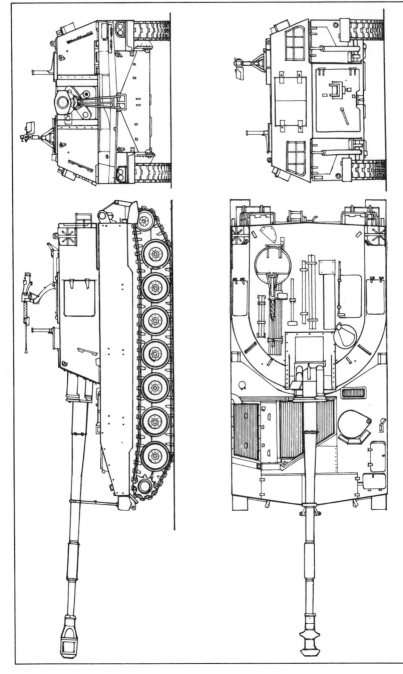

M109A2

1:76 scale

one of the three Royal Artillery field regiments in every armoured division (the other two use Abbots). It is a rather bulky vehicle which makes much use of aluminium armour in its construction, but the bulk does make for plenty of room inside the large turret. In action this houses five of the gun crew (with the driver in his usual position to the left of the hull front), plus another two ammunition handlers who normally travel on an ammunition limber vehicle and remain outside the turret. Two small recoil spades are mounted at the rear for extra firing stability; also at the rear are two sizeable access hatches. The M109A1/M109A2s are provided with all manner of extras such as night driving equipment and a full NBC system.

The 155mm howitzer can fire a wide range of ammunition but the basic type in use is HE (High Explosive). The usual round fired is the American M107 HE, a standard NATO projectile that weighs 42.91 kg. The barrel can be elevated to +75° and depressed to -3°, while the turret has a full 360° traverse.

Throughout its service life the M109 series has been a very successful and reliable weapon with plenty of growth potential built into its design. In fact it now seems probable that yet another re-barrelling programme may be undertaken by the Army for it is now possible to fit barrels with lengths of 45 or even 47 calibres, with corresponding range increases to 24,000m (or more with special ammunition). The delays in getting SP-70 into production have made such a conversion programme very attractive and it is on the cards that the Army will undertake such a course of action. At the time of writing the SP-70 was still scheduled as the eventual M109A2 replacement, but SP-70 is a long way in the future whereas the M109A1/M109A2 is in service now and could be updated at a relatively low cost. As it is, the M109A1/M109A2 is set for many more years of Army use.

155 mm SELF-PROPELLED HOWITZER SP-70

Provisional data — **Armament** 1×155mm howitzer; 1×7.62mm machine-gun. **Crew** 5. **Weight in action** 43,524 kg. **Length, gun forward** 10.235m. **Length of hull** 7.637m. **Engine** MTU MB 871 turbocharged 8-cylinder diesel developing 965 bhp. **Ammunition stowage** 155mm — 32 rounds. **Maximum howitzer range** 24,000m. **Shell weight, L15A1 HE** 43.5 kg.

The 155mm SP-70 self-propelled howitzer has been under development for a long while and can trace its origins back to the same international agreement that produced the towed 155mm FH-70 howitzer. That dates back to the early 1960s and, although the FH-70 is now in service, the SP-70 is still in the development stage with the earliest date now being given for commencement of production as 1988. A great deal of this development delay can be put down to the very nature of international defence agreements, but even so the SP-70 appears to have had more than its fair share of political troubles.

The full development of SP-70 started in 1973 and trials commenced with two prototypes in 1979. More prototypes were produced to take part in a long series of trials that covered almost every aspect of SP-70 use. The project leader for SP-70 is West Germany for they will take the bulk of the projected ouput (West Germany 400, United Kingdom 221 and Italy 90). The production burden has thus been shared out accordingly, but at first glance SP-70 appears to have a high West German content. The hull shows its Leopard tank ancestry and the main engine and final drive come from the Leopard 2 — some of the transmission modules have been adapted from those used on the Marder MICV. The ordnance is also a West German responsibility. The turret, however, is the responsibility of the British, along with the ammunition handling system, sights and traversing mechanism, while the Italians provide the auxiliary power unit, the fuel system and various ordnance controls. The hull is of a new all-welded aluminium construction.

Throughout the design of the SP-70 the emphasis appears to have been on the maximum use of current technology. The ammunition handling system is computer-controlled and is so arranged that the rounds are taken from pre-loaded racks and delivered to the breech for ramming without any handling from the crew. The ammunition can be loaded even when the barrel is at its maximum elevation of +70°. When possible, rounds will be fed into the turret from the outside using a transporter system direct to the breech, since the few rounds carried in the turret itself will soon be expended and the

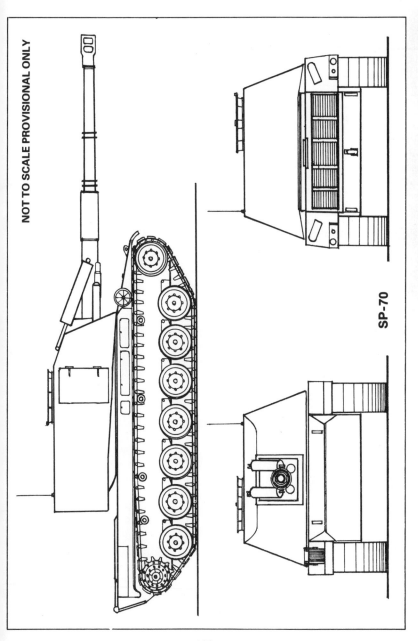

NOT TO SCALE PROVISIONAL ONLY

SP-70

vehicle will then have to retire from action to re-load under cover. This aspect of SP-70 has given rise to a great deal of criticism. In fact, many aspects of SP-70 have caused criticism, although not much of this has come from the Royal Artillery who are anxiously awaiting deliveries. They cannot wait to get SP-70 into service, but the chances that SP-70 will never reach the gunners are now high. The fact is that SP-70 has been subject to so many development delays that it has been overtaken by technological advances elsewhere.

When it was first mooted a maximum range of 24,000m was substantial, but this is now commonplace. Barrels 39 calibres long can now be easily fitted to existing equipments such as the M109A2, while ammunition improvements have made ranges of 30,000m and more attainable by many equipments. The advent of barrels 45 or even 47 calibres long with their attendant range performances has made the 39-calibre barrel of SP-70 look rather 'old hat', and these longer barrels have the advantage that they can be retrofitted relatively easily into existing service equipments. There is one further reason why SP-70 may never reach service, and that is its

A prototype of the 155 mm SP-70 gun.

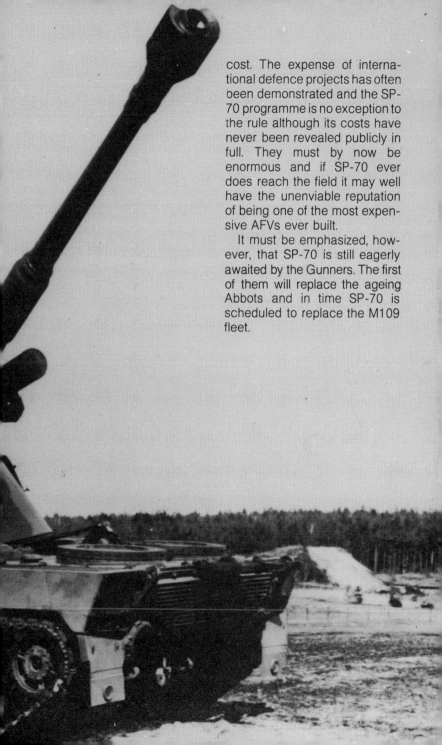

cost. The expense of international defence projects has often been demonstrated and the SP-70 programme is no exception to the rule although its costs have never been revealed publicly in full. They must by now be enormous and if SP-70 ever does reach the field it may well have the unenviable reputation of being one of the most expensive AFVs ever built.

It must be emphasized, however, that SP-70 is still eagerly awaited by the Gunners. The first of them will replace the ageing Abbots and in time SP-70 is scheduled to replace the M109 fleet.

175 mm SELF-PROPELLED GUN M107

Armament 1×175mm M113 gun. **Crew** 5+3. **Weight in action** 28,168 kg. **Length, gun forward** 11.256m. **Length of hull** 5.72m. **Height, top of barrel travelling** 3.679m. **Height, top of mount** 2.809m. **Height, top of hull** 1.475m. **Width** 3.149m. **Track width** 0.457m. **Ground clearance** 0.441m. **Maximum road speed** 56 km/h. **Range, roads** 725 km. **Vertical obstacle** 1.016m. **Maximum gradient** 60%. **Trench crossing** 2.362m. **Fording** 1.066m. **Engine** Detroit Diesel Model 8V-71T turbocharged 8-cylinder diesel developing 405 bhp at 2,300 rpm. **Ammunition stowage** 175mm — 2 rounds. **Maximum gun range** 32,700m. **Shell weight** 66.78 kg.

The 175mm M107 self-propelled long-range gun is one of a family of vehicles that originated back in 1956 although it was 1965-66 before the first of them were purchased for the British Army. The M107 has a very long range of up to 32,700m and is thus used for the counter-battery and long-range interdiction fire roles.

The hull and mounting of the M107 is shared by the 8-in M110A2 self-propelled howitzer and the barrels of the two weapons are designed to

The length of the 175 mm gun on the M107 can be appreciated here.

be interchangeable. The barrel and mounting of the M107 are fully exposed and there is no protection of any kind for the gun and crew, either from the elements or from enemy action. On the move the carriage can carry up to five members of the gun crew with the other three travelling in an ammunition limber vehicle. There is space for only two rounds to be carried on the carriage and only one type of projectile is used with the gun, a 66.78 kg M437A1 or M437A2 HE shell.

In action the gun carriage is stabilized by lowering a recoil spade at the rear, and more stabilization is provided by locking out the carriage suspension. The rounds are taken to a position at the rear of the breech where they are picked up by a hydraulically powered loader assembly which lifts each projectile up to the breech where it is automatically rammed. The rate of fire is rather slow and limited to only one or two rounds a minute. The long barrel can be elevated to a maximum of +65° but traverse on the carriage is limited to 30° either side.

The M107 is scheduled to be replaced in service by the Multiple Launch Rocket System (MLRS (qv)) but it now appears that it will be 1988 at the earliest before this will happen. Until then the M107s will remain in use in the counter-battery role and as such they will form part of the artillery division under the direct control of 1 (BR) Corps. When their replacement by MLRS does take place it is expected that the 175mm barrels will be replaced by 8-in howitzers so that they will then become M110A2s.

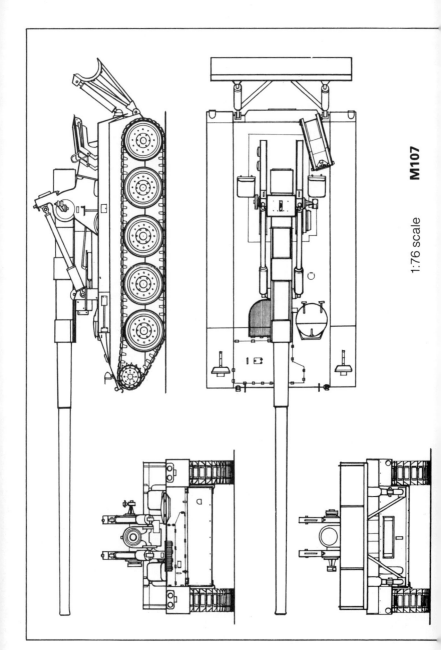

M107

1:76 scale

8-in SELF-PROPELLED HOWITZER M110A2

Armament 1×8-in/203mm M201 howitzer. **Crew** 5+8. **Weight in action** 28,350 kg. **Length, gun forward** 10.73m. **Length of hull** 5.72m. **Height, top of barrel travelling** 3.143m. **Height, top of mount** 2.743m. **Height, top of hull** 1.475m. **Width** 3.149m. **Track width** 0.457m. **Ground clearance** 0.393m. **Maximum road speed** 54.7 km/h. **Range, roads** 523 km. km. **Vertical obstacle** 1.016m. **Maximum gradient** 60%. **Trench crossing** 1.905m. **Fording** 1.066m. **Engine** Detroit Diesel Model 8V-71T turbocharged 8-cylinder diesel developing 405 bhp at 2,300 rpm. **Ammunition stowage** 8-in — 2 rounds. **Maximum howitzer range** 21,300m. **Shell weight, HE** 92.53 kg.

The M110A2 8-in/203mm self-propelled howitzer shares the same carriage and development origins as the 175mm M107, but the howitzer barrel has a much longer development history that can be traced back to World War 1 when the US Army took over a number of British 8-in towed howitzers. The performance of those weapons so impressed the Americans that they retained the type and carried out a great deal of development work on it. When the first M110s were issued to the Army in the late 1960s they were thus equipped with a short-barrelled howitzer (known as the M2A2) that was very similar in many respects to the old British design, right down to the Welin-type breech mechanism.

These early short howitzer barrels have now all been replaced by a much longer barrel known as the M201 which is fitted with a muzzle brake to make the new barre/carriage combination the M110A2. This

An M110A2 camouflaged during a practice shoot in Germany.

The impressive might of the M110A2.

1:76 scale

M110A2

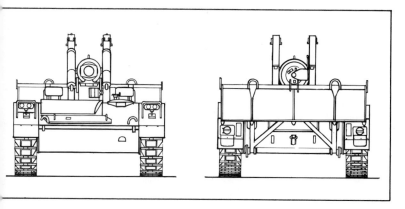

M110A2 has a much longer range than the original M110 self-propelled howitzer but the carriages are still the same.

The M110A2 has a special place within BAOR for it is one of only two nuclear weapon delivery systems used by the Army (the other being the Lance surface-to-surface missile). As such they are organized into one special regiment, 39 Heavy Regiment, RA, under the direct control of the Commander 1 (BR) Corps. There are only a limited number of M110A2s in this regiment, probably about twelve, and in time of war they will be distributed all along the 1 (BR) Corps front in specially prepared 'hides' from which they will 'shoot and scoot', using their mobility to protect them from the expected enemy retaliation.

The M110A2 can fire a HE shell known as the M106 which weighs 92.53 kg. A nuclear shell for the M110A2 is known to have been under development at the Atomic Weapons Establishment at Aldermaston for some years and this may now be in service but the American equivalent is the M422 with a W33 nuclear warhead. This can be fired from the M110A2 to its maximum range of 21,300m. Various other types of American projectile are known to exist but it is thought that the British Army confines its attention to firing HE or nuclear projectiles only.

The M110A2 barrel can be elevated to +65° but traverse on the carriage is confined to 30° either side. The carriage uses the same ammunition lift and loading devices as does the M107 but they are scaled up to suit the heavier projectiles. As many as nine propelling charges can be used. The larger ammunition also means an increase in the size of the crew, which is thirteen. Only five of these can ride on the self-propelled carriage, the rest travelling in the ammunition limber vehicles, and only two projectiles can be carried on the carriage. The M110A2 uses the same rear-mounted recoil spade as the M107.

ARMOURED RECOVERY VEHICLE M578

Armament 1×7.62mm L4A4 machine-gun. **Crew** 3. **Weight in action** 24,470 kg. **Length overall** 6.42m. **Length of hull** 5.588m. **Height to top of cupola** 2.921m. **Width** 3.149m. **Track width** 0.457m. **Ground clearance** 0.47m. **Maximum road speed** 54.7 km/h. **Range, roads** 725 km. **Vertical obstacle** 1.016m. **Maximum gradient** 60%. **Trench crossing** 2.362m. **Fording** 1.066m. **Engine** Detroit Diesel Model 8V-71T turbocharged 8-cylinder diesel developing 405 bhp at 2,300 rpm. **Ammunition stowage** 7.62mm — 1,200 rounds.

When the Army adopted the M109 155mm self-propelled howitzer in 1965 it found itself in the odd situation where none of its existing recovery and repair vehicles could lift the engine pack of the new vehicle. This situation was corrected by purchasing a limited number of M578 light armoured recovery vehicles from the United States.

The M578 is the recovery vehicle component of the series that includes the M107 and M110A2 self-propelled artillery pieces and the M578 uses the same hull and suspension as these two vehicles. In place of the artillery piece the M578 mounts an armoured turret with a crane. The turret also houses the hoisting gear and winch while at the rear is a towing winch with a capicity of 27,000 kg — the hoist winch can lift up to 6,750 kg. The turret can traverse through a full 360°. A 7.62mm L4A4 Bren machine-gun is carried on a pintle over the commander's cupola.

The M578 is used not only with the M107 and M110A2 batteries but also with the M109A2 batteries. It can be used to change barrels as well as engines.

M578 armoured recovery vehicle towing a Stalwart 6 × 6 truck.

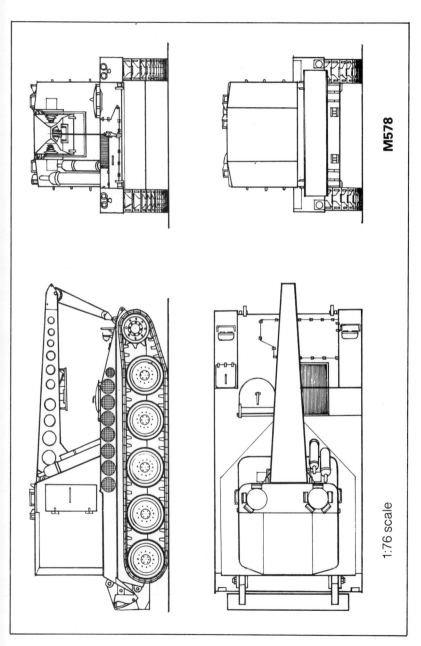

M578

1:76 scale

TRACKED RAPIER

Armament 8×Rapier ground-to-air missiles; 2×5-barrel smoke dischargers; 2×4-barrel smoke dischargers. **Crew** 3. **Weight in action** 14,010 kg. **Length** 6.40m. **Height, tracker raised** 2.78m **Width** 2.80m. **Track width** 0.381m. **Ground clearance** 0.41m. **Maximum road speed** 48 km/h. **Maximum water speed** 5.6 km/h. **Range, roads** 300 km. **Vertical obstacle** 0.609m. **Maximum gradient** 60%. **Trench crossing** 1.676m. **Fording** Amphibious. **Engine** GMC Model 6V-53 6-cylinder diesel developing 210 bhp at 2,800 rpm. **Ammunition stowage** Rapier missiles — 8 on launcher only. **Effective missile range** 6,500m plus.

Tracked Rapier has had one of the more unusual development histories of current Army weapon systems for it had its origins in a British Aerospace attempt to attract orders for the Rapier surface-to-air missile system by mounting it on some form of mobile carriage. Initially the platform chosen was the M578 tracked cargo carrier but so much development was put into this project that the eventual platform emerged as something very different from the original. A large order was then placed by the then Shah of Iran but before they could be delivered the Shah was toppled from his throne (in 1979) and the order was cancelled.

By then the American Food Machinery Corporation (FMC) had produced and delivered the necessary tracked chassis and the Rapier systems had been delivered so British Aerospace were left with a costly project on their hands and no customers. Fortunately for them the British Army had for long been considering how to make the Rapier system more mobile and better-protected and the Tracked Rapier was a handy

Tracked Rapier with aerial raised.

TRACKED RAPIER

1:76 scale

Rear view of Tracked Rapier ready to move.

solution. Tracked Rapier was accordingly ordered for the Army in June 1981.

Tracked Rapier is now being issued to the two Air Defence Regiments of 1 (BR) Corps where they will equip two of the four batteries in each regiment (the other two batteries will continue to use Towed Rapier). In these regiments the Tracked Rapier provides a considerable improvement in air defence capability compared with the older Towed Rapier equipments, for Tracked Rapier can be brought into action within fifteen

seconds of a move and each vehicle has eight Rapiers in armoured bins ready for launching compared with the four of the Towed Rapier. The Tracked Rapier launchers are carried on the rear of a tracked vehicle that owes much to the original M578 cargo carrier chassis but which has been developed so much that it is now called the RCM 748. At the front of the vehicle is an aluminium-armoured crew cab housing the three-men crew in rather cramped surroundings, for the interior is packed with equipment of all kinds. Behind the cab is a compartment containing the air-conditioning unit and heater and a diesel generator identical to that used on the Chieftain MBT. Over the missile launch bins is the missile

Tracked Rapier (left) with an M548 ammunition resupply vehicle.

tracking radar while in a central radome between the launch bins is a surveillance radar. The entire vehicle can be rendered fully amphibious by raising wading screens all around the vehicle, but these are not normally fitted.

The Rapier missiles are the same as those used with the Towed Rapier. They are 2.24m long and weigh 42.6 kg each. With Tracked Rapier their minimum range is 400m and their maximum effective range is over 6,500m. Their hit rate is stated to be over seventy per cent.

Getting Tracked Rapier into service has set the Army a few problems. One headache is that the system is so packed with black boxes and other equipment that simply gaining access for maintenance or repair is a major task. One example is that to change an engine involves removing all the gear in the cab and the cab itself, a job that takes over 29 man hours. The tracks have proved to be very prone to wear with each set lasting less than 300 km, but a new design of track should improve this situation. The diesel generator is rather prone to emit clouds of fumes that give away the vehicle's position, but again this is being put right. The net result is that the Tracked Rapiers take a good deal of looking after and are accordingly centred around one major base with all the necessary repair and maintenance facilities.

In the field Tracked Rapier is supplied with fresh loads of Rapier missiles by unarmoured M578 tracked cargo carriers, each with a crew of two and racks for twenty missiles. Each Tracked Rapier vehicle will have its own M578 support/supply vehicle. The M578 is also used for the Forward Area Support Team (FAST) repair vehicle which will carry repair and test equipment, a front-mounted crane and a crew of two.

Although Tracked Rapier is now in service it is still the subject of more development. A new on-board command computer is under considera-tion and a thermal imaging facility is possible. The present optical control system may be augmented by a new tracker, optical, thermally-enhanced (TOTE) known as Darkfire, and other such items are in the pipeline.

MULTIPLE LAUNCH ROCKET SYSTEM

Armament 12×227mm ballistic rockets. **Crew** 3. **Weight in action** 25,191 kg. **Length travelling** 6.972m. **Height travelling** 2.617m. **Height, launcher elevated** 5.92m. **Width travelling** 2.972m. **Track width** 0.533m. **Ground clearance** 0.43m. **Maximum road speed** 64 km/h. **Range, roads** 483 km. **Vertical obstacle** 0.914m. **Maximum gradient** 60%. **Trench crossing** 2.29m. **Fording** 1.02m. **Engine** Cummins VTA-903 turbocharged 8-cylinder diesel developing 500 bhp at 2,400rpm. **Ammunition stowage** 227mm rockets — 12 on launcher.

Rocket — **Body diameter** 0.227m. **Length** 3.96m. **Weight** 308 kg. **Maximum range** 30,000m plus.

The Multiple Launch Rocket System, or MLRS as it is usually known, started life as an American project but has now blossomed into an

Dramatic view of a missile being launched from a Multiple Launch Rocket System.

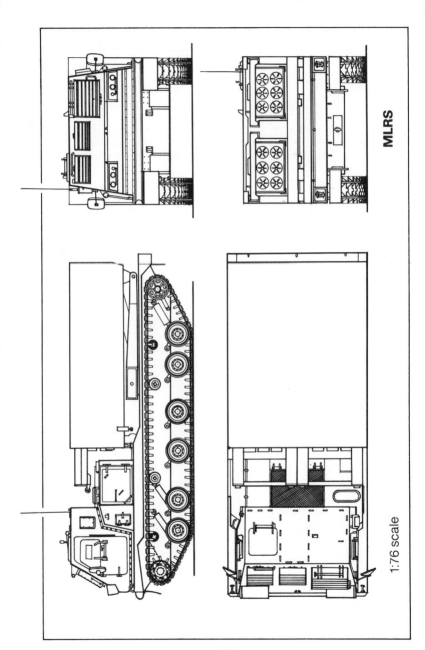

MLRS

1:76 scale

One of the Multiple Launch Rocket Systems soon to enter British service.

international programme. It was originally a 1976 US Army project that involved a 'shoot-off' between various designs and concepts until the system emerged in its present form in 1980. Since then MLRS has entered service with the US Army but its planned introduction into service by other NATO nations, including the United Kingdom, West Germany, Italy and France, has been beset by the delays that international defence projects seem to engender. The NATO project has been delayed further by the fact that it is planned to produce MLRS in Europe and the 'who does what?' division of the production contracts.

To date the British Army has received only four training MLRS systems and at the time of writing even they were still 'in the supply system'. The current plan is that the Army will start to get its MLRS equipments during 1988 but even this forecast may turn out to be somewhat optimistic as the European production plans are still in their early stages. However, the Army is anxious to obtain MLRS as soon as possible for it will be one of the most important NATO land weapon systems of the coming decade.

MLRS has been developed to provide a powerful long-range artillery system that will literally cover the rear areas behind enemy lines with fire. To do this MLRS fires a 227mm ballistic rocket to a range of over 30,000m and the idea is to saturate any target area with explosive. Accordingly the MLRS rockets are fired in salvos from a launcher that can hold twelve in two pre-packed containers, each containing six rockets. The containers are put into the launchers by means of a power-loading system and the launchers are carried to the launch position on a tracked chassis which is based on the American M2 Bradley infantry vehicle but which has been much modified, especially in the suspension area. The MLRS launch vehicle carries a crew of three in a forward-mounted armoured cab and each vehicle contains its own fire control and position reference systems. It also has its own self-loading crane system to load rocket containers, which also act as launch pods, into the launcher frame. Once loaded the launcher can be traversed and elevated to the correct angle for firing. The rockets may be launched one at a time although they will usually be fired in salvos.

The free-flight ballistic rockets each have a warhead containing 644 fragmentation bomblets, each weighing 0.23 kg. Over the target area these bomblets will cover a wide area and each can penetrate up to 100mm of armour — the effects can be imagined. This type of warhead is not the only one envisaged for one containing 28 AT-2 miniature anti-tank mines is under development in West Germany and another with a self-guiding millimetric radar terminal guidance system is in the early stages of development in the United States.

The problem for the British Army is that this is still all in the future. When MLRS does arrive it will replace the current M107 175mm long-range guns, and it is anticipated that at least two regiments will be formed.

INDEX